THEY OPENED THE WEST

THEY
OPENED
THE
WEST

An Anthology by the
Western Writers of America
Edited by
Tom W. Blackburn

DOUBLEDAY & COMPANY, INC.

GARDEN CITY, NEW YORK

1967

Library of Congress Catalog Card Number 67-10418

FOREWORD

For many years it was fashionable among historians and laymen alike to regard the American West as the nation's heroic epoch, peopled by larger-than-life figures characteristic of the legend and folklore of any fabled time. However, in the past decade the far more exciting detail of true historical perspective has begun to emerge.

Men, women, and events have begun to materialize from the sentimental morass of Western legend in the simple human dimension which was theirs in life. For the first time readers are being afforded opportunity to come to some understanding of America and Americans today in the revealing light of what they actually were, individually and collectively, a century ago.

Many elements are responsible for this more accurate view of a heritage of which we all are justly proud. The painstaking work of a new generation of devoted professional researchers and historians has brought much new material to light in a more precise correlation of men and times. A tremendous expansion of interest in matters pertaining to the Western era among serious students at all levels as well as the general public has made possible publication of a great many works heretofore unavailable. But perhaps the most effective effort has been that made by the professional authors who comprise the membership of the Western Writers of America.

For more than ten years these men and women, working in almost every medium, have dedicated themselves and their work to presentation of the American West as living history of a stirring time in which human virtues and frailties intermingled in the forging of principles and traditions by which a vast majority of the people of this nation is guided or influenced today. This volume, another in a continuing series issued annually by the Western Writers of America, is a gripping evidence of that effort.

Specifically, THEY OPENED THE WEST is an anthology of fact and fiction—much of it especially written for this volume and appearing for the first time herein—which outlines westward expansion in terms of the adventures associated with the roads and rivers, communications and pioneering enterprises, which quite literally opened the way for the vast mass migration which followed. The selections have been made on a basis of sound scholarship, integrity in time, place, and problem, and above all—a must in any work bearing the seal of the Western Writers of America—top-flight storytelling.

To the student wishing to flesh out the bones of assigned history texts, to the legion of Western enthusiasts, and to the general reader who relishes a well-told tale, I highly commend this compendium of American adventure.

TOM BLACKBURN
Newport Beach, Calif.

CONTENTS

THEY OPENED THE WEST

High-Water Highway

BY CLIFF FARRELL

In 1806, as a result of agitation starting about 1800, an act of Congress approved the route for a proposed road into what was then known as "the West." Contracts for construction were let in 1811 but the War of 1812 delayed commencement of construction until 1815. Built with Federal funds along an Indian trail and surfaced with crushed stone, the first section (the Cumberland Road) was completed from Cumberland, Maryland, to Wheeling, West Virginia. Between 1825 and 1833, due largely to the efforts of Henry Clay, who clearly saw the imperative need for a public highway to overtake the expanding frontier, it was extended to Columbus, Ohio. Problems of maintenance and repair forced the government to turn older portions over to the states through which it ran, but new construction continued and it reached Vandalia, Illinois, in 1840 and St. Louis, its final terminal, shortly thereafter. The old National Road is closely followed by modern U.S. 40.

—T.W.B.

AT least nature was on Lafe Nelson's side the day he was forced to begin his fight for independence. It was early May, and the persistent rains had tapered off, letting the sunshine drench the lush new Ohio country in golden wine that went giddily to a man's head.

If he were a singing man he would have given voice as he unsuspectingly drove his six-horse team westward over the hilly, muddy, dog-trot trace that was newly named as the National Road. But he couldn't carry a tune in a basket, so he let the whole expanding, greening world and its birds in the field sing and whistle for him.

He walked beside his high-wheeled freight wagon because he preferred to meet the miles with the striding challenge of his own legs. In the hardest going he put his shoulder to the load—not that his Conestoga-bred horses needed the help, but to enjoy the opposition of weight against his strength.

With eyes as blue as a sunny sea, and tawny hair, he wore his striped breeches bagged over the tops of his boots, and his chest filled his butternut shirt to the bursting point. He was five weeks out of Baltimore over the old Cumberland Road, and his wagon carried a load of freight consigned to merchants at a place called Zanesville, which, according to the milestones, was now only some five days ahead of him.

He had passed the last gang of men who were cracking limestone rocks to surface the National Road into a passable thirty-foot highway that would extend someday, it was said, even to the Mississippi River at St. Louis. Shortly afterward Lafe had ferried the Ohio River at Wheeling. Since then his team had been plowing through a muddy, untamed road.

However, other teams were also bucking the muddy going, for he had been following the freshening wheel tracks of a wagon and a spike team all morning. Then, from the crest of a hill, he sighted the outfit he was overtaking. It was a small, canvas-hooded wagon of the type settlers used, and it was mired in a mudhole at the foot of the descent.

Lafe braked down the hill and pulled up to survey the situation. The settler's wagon carried a load of furniture and possibles that bulged the canvas tilt into knotty shape, and it was down below the hubs in the bog hole.

The three horses stood hipshot in the mud, waiting with the air of animals that were accustomed to this sort of thing. A plump, motherly woman, wearing a calico sunbonnet, sat placidly on a tree stump in the dry, a knitting basket on her lap, the needles busy on a half-finished sock. Some distance back in the woods Lafe glimpsed a smallish man stalking some quarry, a squirrel gun in his hands.

The woman with the knitting said, "'Morning, young man! It's a purely beautiful day."

Before Lafe could agree, a girl appeared from the woods, dragging lengths of stout fallen tree limbs. She had her skirt and petticoat pinned up clear of the mud, and beneath these she wore practical cowhide boots that were well coated with Ohio mud.

Her sunbonnet hung on her back. She was hot and in a hurry, and one strand of hair that was a rich chestnut shade kept falling over her nose and she kept blowing it away with explosive impatience. She was, Lafe noticed, endowed by nature with a very nice figure, and she had the kind of lively brown eyes that always seemed excited.

She glanced at Lafe and said, "I'm lightening the load so we can pull out of this hole, and you'd better do the same before you try crossing."

She began tossing the tree limbs into position in the mud to afford firmer footing for the task ahead. She lifted her voice and called, "Paw! Come and give a hand!"

Lafe regarded her with a respect he did not usually offer the feminine sex. He had long ago come to the conclusion that girls, particularly the comely ones, became clinging and helpless whenever a man showed up. Their sole purpose in life, he had decided, was to trap a husband and bind him to one spot.

This one seemed to be an exception. "No use going to all that trouble, miss," he said kindly. "I'll double-team you out of that."

He got a stout rope from the jockey box. Freeing his team from the wagon, he drove to solid ground beyond the bog and hooked up to the mired wagon. The girl took charge of the spike team efficiently, and the wagon groaned and lurched free, rolling easily to firm land as Lafe's sorrels leaned into the job.

Then Lafe reversed the procedure; using the spike team for auxiliary power, he and the girl yanked his heavy wagon through the mud, though it was touch and go for a minute as to whether they would make it.

The girl blew the annoying strand of hair off her nose again. She wasn't very big, but she was as active as a minnow and had a neat dust of freckles above the bridge of her small nose.

She got her reticule from the wagon. "You went to the most

trouble," she said. "I believe twenty-five cents would be a fair price for your part of the bargain."

Lafe backed away from the coin she had dug from the reticule. "Pay?" he protested, shocked. "As far as I'm concerned, miss, we're even."

She put away the coin. "Well, that's settled," she said. "But it would have been a clear profit for you."

She sized up Lafe's team and wagon approvingly, and appraised Lafe's brawn also. "How many tons?" she asked, referring to the wagon.

"Three ton, four hundred," Lafe said proudly. "Mostly hardware, hogshead of white sugar, and Jamaica rum for delivery in Zanesville."

"What is your haulage charge?" she asked.

"Two dollars a hundred," Lafe said, a trifle shortly, for he usually did not discuss business matters with women.

She pursed her lips. "The most of them charge two dollars and twenty-five cents," she stated. "Take my advice and ask for more when you load for the haul back to Baltimore."

Lafe tried to wither her with a frown. "Two dollars is a fair price," he said, settling the matter. "Anyway, I'm not going back to Baltimore."

"You're settling in Zanesville?"

"I didn't say that," Lafe said petulantly. "I own my own wagon and team and took on this load to help pay expenses. I figure I'll keep going west."

"West? Why? There's plenty of land to be had here in Ohio."

"I've got my own reasons," Lafe said vaguely. How could he tell her he just wanted to keep on going to see what lay over the next rise?

"You're just like my paw," she sniffed. "Always imagining things will be better somewhere else, when there's opportunity right under his nose."

Paw returned out of the woods now, carrying his squirrel gun. He was a mild-eyed, easy-voiced man in homespun. He shook hands with Lafe. He was Thomas Morgan, he said, from New

York State, and this was his wife, Hattie, and his daughter, Melodie.

He expressed no surprise at finding the wagon safely out of the mudhole. Evidently he depended upon Melodie. "Seen the tracks of a doe," he said, "but they was hours old."

"I knocked over a fat one evening before last," Lafe said. "I got a saddle and ham hanging in the wagon."

"Did you happen to notice anything that looked like good farmland?" Melodie demanded pointedly of her father.

Mrs. Morgan intervened. "Now, don't you always be nagging your paw, Melodie," she chided mildly. "My land, we'll find something sooner or later. Paw likes to hunt."

"I hear there's unclaimed level land out in Indiana," Tom Morgan said. "Black soil, and deep."

"Indiana!" the daughter sniffed. "It won't be any better soil than in Ohio."

"I aim to pass through Indiana," Lafe remarked. "Fact is, I might even go beyond the Mississippi. I'd like to get me a buffalo, just for the fun of it."

Tom Morgan regarded Lafe admiringly. "Man!" he breathed wistfully.

"Buffalo!" Melodie said disparagingly. "All you'll do is be scalped by wild Indians."

Lafe became aware of the approaching jingle of trace chains. A heavy, Pittsburg-built freighter was rolling down the hill toward the mudhole.

Lafe yelled a warning to the driver but the man figured he could make it if he hit the bog fast enough. He failed. Midway across the trap his outfit mired down despite the floundering of the six-horse team.

"I'll double-team you, friend," Lafe offered.

Melodie Morgan spoke up: "The charge will be fifty cents."

Lafe cringed but the mired freighter didn't seem offended. "All right," the man said. "I've got a delivery date to make and have to pay a penalty for every day I'm late."

Lafe hauled the outfit from the mud, and accepted the coin

the man handed over. He felt mighty small but he couldn't refuse without its reflecting on the girl.

After the Pittsburg wagon had gone on its way Melodie eyed the mudhole speculatively. "A person with a team could do right well here, double-hauling mired outfits," she remarked pointedly to Lafe.

She was also smiling at him very sweetly. Panic suddenly shook Lafe as he realized what was in the wind. She was so blasted pretty the thought of what she was up to made queer tremors race up his spine.

Then he saw pity in Tom Morgan's eyes. Tom Morgan figured he would never see a buffalo, now. Not now, with Melodie setting her cap for him.

"I'm going west," Lafe said in the voice of a man who is his own master. "That's what I'm doing."

They traveled on together for the rest of the day. Melodie spent her time walking with Lafe. Whenever she came in close contact the tremors began running through him almost uncontrollably. There was a faint, heady fragrance in the air that he couldn't identify. It was the clean perfume of fresh-cut cedar, and the memory of exotic spices and the promise of pink rosebuds all blended into something that was new and amazing and started a man to dreaming dangerously.

Then he would be brought back to reality, for she kept busily inspecting the surroundings as the road carried them onward through the greening hills.

"Now *there's* a stretch of land that hasn't been taken," she would say. "Wild hay meadows ready for the plow, and timber in the uplands for a man to build barns and a home."

Lafe drove doggedly on. He was glad when sundown came. Melodie picked the campsite. Lafe's will turned to water when he tried to say he was moving on to a place of his own choosing. So he unharnessed and put the stock out to graze while camp was being set up. He contributed his venison to the evening meal. He knew he was playing with fire but he was sure of his own strength.

Melodie had taken off her cowhide boots and had on a fresh calico dress; she'd done something to her hair that made a man want to touch its warm softness. She was quick and sure as she helped her mother with the Dutch oven and the skillets. The balmy spring darkness was closing in, and her shadow followed him, no matter where he moved.

Lafe got his jug from the wagon when the women weren't looking. He gave Mr. Morgan a wink, and they drifted into the shadows and had a deep and soul-satisfying snort each. It was rich, keel-aged Jamaica, good for snakebite, the ague, and all the ills of the mind that beset mankind. It drove new warmth and a new courage through them.

"I figured I always wanted to notch a sight on a buffalo, too," Tom Morgan said at last, and sighed.

Melodie called, "Food's ready!" And they hurried back with appetites whetted to razor edge.

But hoofs sounded on the trail, and a Concord coach carrying a mail flag appeared in the far reflection of the cook fire. Lafe could see the driver and the faces of passengers, and all of them were sniffing the wonderful aroma from the fire.

"Howdy, folks," the driver called. "That grub smells mighty appetizing. I've got five hungry men here, includin' myself, what ain't had a bite since forenoon. We're hours behind schedule an' won't reach a roadhouse before midnight. We'd be happy to pay well for a meal if you could accommodate us."

Lafe and Mr. Morgan glanced at each other, their hearts sinking.

"Well, I don't know," Melodie said.

"Twenty-five cents a head," the driver offered ingratiatingly. "A dollar and a quarter for the lot of us."

"I guess we can wait a little longer," Melodie said, and had the grace to give Lafe and her father an apologetic look. "It won't take a minute to fix us another meal."

But what Lafe and Mr. Morgan ate was smokedside and warmed-over biscuits, for the stage passengers cleaned up all the venison.

Melodie forced Lafe to accept a share of the proceeds, pointing out that it was his venison which had been used. "Money just seems to fall into a person's lap in a country that's building up," she said.

Lafe then and there made up his mind to make the break the next day. But when morning came the rain had set in again. With the trail a quagmire it would be heartless to abandon them, for they would likely need more help in the mudholes during the day.

"Rain," Melodie said, "is what makes Ohio beautiful. Why, they say that out west it's nothing but a starving desert. Skeletons every foot of the way. And wild Indians. Ugh!"

They breakfasted under a stretched wagon sheet, and it was a solid meal, for Melodie went to extra pains to make up for the venison. And the gay petticoat she wore was a pretty thing on a dull day and fitted very snugly in the most fetching places.

As they were breaking camp Melodie made a great issue over a brass-bound sandalwood chest that had been unloaded, evidently by mistake, from the Morgan wagon. Lafe gathered from Melodie's excitement that the chest contained whatever valuables the Morgans owned. Melodie saw to it personally that the chest was disguised in a weather-stained piece of canvas tarp and stowed carefully in their wagon.

They made slow progress through the mud, and it was mid-afternoon when they reached a stream called Middle Fork. It was tree-lined and notched deep in abrupt hills. Normally, a wagon probably could ford it without more than splashing the reach, but now Middle Fork was fifty yards from bank to bank, with high and rolling mud.

"Looks like we'll be hung up until she goes down," Mr. Morgan said.

"At least," Melodie said, "it will give us a chance to look around."

And, with a little more time at her disposal, she got together another meal that topped all her past performances. Hog jowls boiled with new, tender, rain-wet watercress, hominy grits, and johnnycake, pickled preserves, and, above all, potlikker that was nectar.

Lafe was desperate after that meal. He knew its memory would cling to him like that fragrance of cedar and spices and new roses.

Afterward he did some looking around on his own. He found what he wanted, but it wasn't farmland. Upstream, at a bend, higher floods in the past had heaped up a tangle of driftwood which included seasoned trees of all sizes that were easy to work.

He hurried back to the wagon, got out his tarp-covered handy box, and laid out his tools.

"What—?" Melodie demanded.

"I'm going to build a raft," Lafe said. "I figure to cross the stream tomorrow. It'll save maybe a week's time."

Melodie was opposed to it, but she didn't say so in words. She made Lafe understand, however, in that aggravating way females have when they want to make a man feel in the wrong, that she thought he was going to unnecessary bother.

But by the next midmorning, when the raft was beginning to take shape, she seemed to change her mind.

"If I were you I'd make it stronger," she said.

"It'll hold long enough for our purposes," Lafe protested.

"No use taking a chance," she argued.

So they doubled the bracing. Melodie had other criticisms, so that by the time they had finished it the raft was a far more permanent proposition than Lafe had intended.

More freighters and travelers were camped now on both banks, waiting for Middle Fork to recede. A fast express wagon was among the westbound contingent. The driver of this rig was nervous and worried. Melodie brought him to where Lafe was putting the finishing touches on the raft.

"I'm carrying a hundred gross of iced bluepoint oysters, worth a pretty penny," the man explained. "That ice is melting fast. If you'll ferry me across right now I'd be plenty obliged."

Lafe dubiously eyed the rainy twilight that was setting in.

"Well, I reckon I can do it, since you're in such a bad fix, stranger," he said.

"I'll pay a dollar," the express driver offered.

"Two dollars," Melodie spoke up flatly. "You're getting special service, and it has to be done in darkness."

"Two it is," the man agreed readily, "an' glad to pay it."

Lafe glared at the girl. "Miss—" he began to thunder. Then he realized he was the only one dissatisfied with the bargain.

He swam the river with a light line, pulled his greased rope across, and moored it solidly. After that it was easy. With the raft slung to the cable by a sliding halter, the current helped drift it across, with only a little poling necessary.

Pitch flares lighted the way. Lafe ferried the express wagon across and Melodie accompanied him on the initial journey. She made a dicker with a Baltimore-bound stage driver who was flood-bound on the west bank with six passengers, so that the return trip was equally profitable.

Other travelers were in a hurry, also, and Melodie set a scale of prices for humans, stock, and vehicles. Lafe and Tom Morgan worked until midnight moving fares across the stream. And more were waiting to cross in daylight.

Later in the tent Melodie counted out the profits. "And this is only the start," she said. "Why, a person could be well fixed in no time running a ferry here. And you aren't risking dying of thirst in that terrible desert out west."

"Won't need a ferry when the water drops," Lafe pointed out.

"People would rather ferry than chance a ford any time," she said. "You wait and see."

Lafe knew now why she had badgered him into building the raft solid. She just didn't understand how he felt about the buffalo.

"The ferry is yours," he said suddenly. "I'm moving on tomorrow."

He didn't have the courage to look at her. Melodie said, "Oh!" And she let the last coin dribble from her fingers. She just sat there, looking at nothing. But she didn't try to talk him out of it. . . .

Lafe got an early start the next morning. He was up an hour before false dawn. Action was better than lying sleepless in his blankets. Melodie was up, too, and insisted on cooking his breakfast—white-flour fry cakes that were crisp on the edges and so feather-light they almost floated in the maple syrup; center-cut ham steaks, and eggs that she picked up in barter from some passing farmer; cornbread and honey.

Afterward Lafe paused a couple of times as he was harnessing. But each time he forced himself to keep on going. Melodie and her father packed his gear into the wagon while he was at his task. Then he was loaded and ready. He shook hands with Mrs. Morgan and with Tom. Then came the critical moment, after they had ferried him to the west shore.

"Well, good-by, Miss Melodie," he said, and his voice was a croak. "I'm hoping you have the best of luck with the ferry."

She gave him her hand. It was small, and it was shaking, too, and it was cold, but Lafe dropped it as though it were a live fire chunk.

He popped the whip with violence, arousing his startled horses. He didn't look back. He didn't dare.

The sun was coming up, and the larks were awake. Lafe was aware again of that heavenly fragrance of spring—the cedar and spices and promise of pink roses.

He kept going doggedly onward, heading for a country where, over some horizon, he would finally see the buffalo and the wild Indians. With each mile of distance he told himself that he was more secure in his escape and his independence. But his heart would not sing with the world, now.

Three days later he pulled into the bustling settlement called Zanesville. He inquired his way, and began unloading his cargo at the stores of the various merchants to whom the items were consigned.

His handy box, wearing its canvas cover, was often in his way as he delved into the cargo. Each time he moved it he became giddily aware of that fragrance of spring which had followed him so tantalizingly.

Suddenly he jerked off the tarp and stood staring incredulously. It wasn't his handy box at all! It was the brass-bound sandalwood chest that had caused Melodie so much anxiety in their overnight camps.

The chest and his handy box were about the same size, and both had been tarp-covered. It was easy now to see how the blunder had been made. He could imagine the consternation in the Morgan family if they had discovered the loss of their valuables.

Possession of that chest was dangerous in more ways than one to his peace of mind. It was like having Melodie right here with him. His first thought was that he should return it in care of some eastbound freighter. Then he realized he didn't dare risk it. He would have to backtrack to Middle Fork to make sure they received it safely.

He slept beside the precious object that night, his fowling piece within reach. And as long as he was heading east he took on a load of crated pottery ware consigned to Wheeling. A few days' additional delay made no real difference. Furthermore, the cargo would make Melodie understand that delivering the chest in person was not the only reason for his reappearance.

The weather had turned warm and the countryside was blooming into full leaf. The road had dried and the streams were returning rapidly to normal as he drove eastward. Lafe guessed the ferry project would be done for at Middle Fork, but he guessed wrong.

It was late afternoon of the third day when he let his team pause at the top of the last hill looking down on the ford. The raft was still in operation, moving a wagon to the east bank of the stream in spite of the fact Middle Fork was obviously low now and easily fordable. Another wagon was waiting to be moved across. Tom Morgan was using the pole, and Lafe glimpsed a small, active figure in calico on the far shore.

His mouth tightened in critical grimness. To his way of thinking Melodie was taking advantage of the haste and gullibility of travelers by operating a ferry at a stream where wagons could cross without costing people a cent.

Well, he reflected, he would not be a party to any such humbug. He popped his horses into motion. He was mad and he had a sensation of empty disillusionment. The fragrance of cedar and rosebuds and spice was a fraud, too, like the ferry. It was perfume and nothing else. He knew now that Melodie was the one who had spirited that chest into his wagon. She had wanted to lure him back into her reach.

He put his surprised team to a trot; he saw Melodie come running as he neared the ford. She was shouting something, waving her arms. And her father, who had just finished discharging his fare ashore, was yelling also.

Lafe ignored them. Naturally Melodie didn't want anybody demonstrating that a wagon could ford the stream. That would end a profitable business. Lafe hit Middle Fork at a full trot. Water flew high from the legs of the team, drenching him, but in his anger he did not even notice the chill.

The water also blinded him, but he was aware that his outfit was bogging down. His vision cleared, and it was too late to do anything about it. His horses were floundering wildly and uttering terrible snorting explosions of terror.

Quicksand!

Lafe realized the truth. The recent high water must have gouged out whatever solid bottom there had been at the ford. The lead team was now down to the saddles. The swings and wheelers were sinking deeper despite their churning.

Lafe leaped between the wheelers, and after a lung-straining moment he managed to free the swingles from the doubletree. Then he released the pole chains. The six animals fought their way clear of the wagon, but they were hopelessly snarled in the harness. Lafe got out his sheath knife and plunged among them, slashing at tugs and hame straps, hoping to release the horses and give them a chance to make their way to shore.

He was blinded by churning water and appalled by the maelstrom of hoofs and lurching bodies. Coming up for air, he glimpsed the raft bearing down on them, with Melodie's eyes big and frightened against the pallor of her face, and her voice screaming, "Lafe!"

Then a hoof struck him on the back of the head. He vaguely saw Tom Morgan poling violently and Melodie leaping from the raft, which was still out of reach. Then he sank among the floundering horses into blackness.

He drifted out of it after a time. He was lying on solid land, and Melodie Morgan was working on him. Her calico dress was soaked and clinging in a manner that was shocking, but nice to see. Then Lafe went back to sleep again.

It was next midmorning before he really became aware of events. His head cleared rapidly, though it felt twice its normal size. He was in the Morgan tent, lying on Melodie's blankets. The whole family was present.

"Melodie pulled you out from among them horses, son," Mr. Morgan said proudly. "Dove right into that buzz saw before I could stop her and got you to the raft."

Lafe looked at Melodie, and he wished he were dead.

"We got your horses out, too," her father said. "And even saved the wagon. Got a span of oxen and they eased the wagon out without pullin' it apart. Lucky you was packing pottery. Water won't hurt it. A freighter come by empty so I turned the load over to him to deliver at Wheeling. I figured you, wantin' to get out west, would like it that way."

Lafe said, looking at Melodie, "I figured things out wrong."

Melodie arose suddenly and left the tent. Lafe couldn't blame her. He guessed she knew he had expected to expose the ferry as a fraud. Mr. Morgan looked uncomfortable. "Well, I reckon you'll get to see them buffalo after all. Why'd you come back this way at all, son?"

"The chest," Lafe said. "The sandalwood chest with all your valuables in it. I found it in my wagon at Zanesville."

"Valuables?" Tom Morgan snorted. "You mean them things Melodie keeps in her hope chest. It was only a bunch of linen and doilies and jimcracks a girl saves up ag'in the time she traps a husband. Melodie's dryin' the stuff an' ironin' it for storin' back in the chest again."

Lafe didn't say anything. There was nothing to be said. . . .

He was fit to travel the following morning. Tom Morgan helped him harness up. Mrs. Morgan kissed him and wished him Godspeed.

But Melodie didn't even come around to say good-by. And Lafe didn't blame her for that, either. He put the team slowly in motion and drove west again away from Middle Fork. He was heading toward the buffalo, and this time there was no turning back. But all Lafe could think of was the loneliness that would await him in the Western desert.

He didn't even walk. He rode apathetically in the bow of a wagon box, surrounded only by the hollow rumble of the empty wagon and the vacancy of his own future.

It was a long time before he became aware of something heartbreakingly familiar: that breath of spring, again—the clean tang of cedar and roses and spices.

Suddenly he turned. The big wagon was not entirely empty. The sandalwood chest was aboard again. And sitting upon the chest was Miss Melodie Morgan. She had her hands demurely clasped in her lap and she was wearing her best bonnet.

"I decided," she said, her voice a trembling whisper, "that I wanted to see a buffalo, too."

The horses kept plodding along, for Lafe was busy. He had his arms full of something that was small and alive, and warm and far more fragrant than spring.

After a long time they were sitting together in the bow, very close together, and Lafe drove with one hand. The larks were singing and Lafe's heart was singing with them.

A stretch of open meadow appeared, and Melodie saw it. She started to speak. Then she looked at Lafe and closed her mouth determinedly. She smiled guiltily at him.

"It'll still be here if we come back this way," Lafe said. "I'll say when and where we stop and settle."

"Yes, Lafe," Melodie said meekly. But she couldn't help looking back over her shoulder at that piece of land, and marking it in her memory for future reference.

The Proud

BY LUCIA MOORE

The deliberate instigators of the first legends—the pathfinders and discoverers of a vast, unmapped land—the true paladins of the West— were a jealously select band of men who probably never numbered more than a hundred individuals of any consequence in their hard-won profession. They were the fur trappers and traders—the "mountain men." It is a curious paradox of history that the artificial international demand of fops, dandies, and fine gentlemen for elegant headpieces felted from the fur of American beaver financed these rugged, often uncouth, generally improbable adventurers in the feats of daring, endurance, and frequent rascality by which they seized an unpeopled personal empire stretching from the Rocky Mountains to the Pacific. Living upon equal and usually amicable terms with the fiercest of the Indians, these few score held and exploited their trackless domain from the end of the War of 1812 until beaver headgear began to decline in fashion a decade before the discovery of gold in California. They were a single generation and they certainly had no such purpose in mind, but they opened the route of almost every Western highway in use today. It is impossible to now grasp either their motive or the scope of their accomplishment without some understanding of them as individuals, for they were in a very real sense larger than life as we know it today. Yet their stamp is upon us, still. Their lusty love of land and life has become an American hallmark in the eyes of all nations. —T.W.B.

THE mountain man waded a small stream, feeling the deep silence of a forest furred with snow. Tall and wiry, wary too, Joe Meek was wanting beaver in his traps this morning, though there was not much reason to hope. Beaver were getting as wary as a fur trapper and nearly as smart. But Joe was a cheerful critter. The forests were his, and the blue snows and the far, purpled peaks. Squirrels came from the trees to tell him to mind his own business and he told them right back to mind theirs, rounded a turn in the icy water, and found his traps.

Hell. No beaver. Maybe it was like Doc Newell said—the beaver windfall had gone to smithereens; it looked as if the rascals sensed it and didn't bother to let themselves get caught, but it was not their fault that the world's fool men had tossed beaver hats away and were peacocking around in a new kind of headgear.

Turning back, Joe considered Newell and his talk about the West beyond these Shining Mountains, about farms, and even about plowing. Farms. Imagine me behind a plow, Meek scorned. If I hadn't seen Pa's slaves at it I wouldn't know which end of a plow was the hind end. Just the same, if it was plow or starve I'd likely plow, west in Oregon or home in Virginia.

He felt near starvation now and wished for his demijohn of Taos lightning, for strengthening wind tore at his buckskins, his feet were two iced stumps in his buffalo-skin boots that in winter he wore turned outside in. The wind shook him the way it shook snow from the aspens. If Bob Newell had been there to remind him that only three days ago Nez Percés had warmed him and fed him he would have called Doc a liar.

What about this Oregon thing? Could a mountain man live there? A mountain man was a breed, the way an Indian was a breed. The Jim Clymans, the Bridgers, the Newells, and the Meeks, too, walked, talked, spied, thought, fought like Indians; dressed like Indians; and damn nigh were Indians. A mountain man could see behind a tree and through a black sky and under water, and when it came to it he could never leave his solitude. The traders, now, could; they were the hard ones. A mountain man was the tool, the worked-to-the-bone slave, the rod that brought down lightning in the shape of money to the fur companies. Wagh. All you've got, Joe Meek, to see you through with your skin is a trap and a laugh, a joke and another pair of moccasins to put on when these boots play out. Last pair of moccasins is about gone. Get yourself a squaw and stay where you belong. Oregon is full of missionaries and preachers; it ain't likely they'd put up with your jokes.

Meek had been blessed earlier with a handsome young squaw,

a Snake woman he had managed to come by in a kind of Joe
Meek way, part luck and part slick management. She was the
Indian wife of Milt Sublette, and Joe, watching Isobel make
Sublette comfortable and lolling as any Virginia gentleman,
could only dream, then give up. The trouble was, Milt Sublette was Joe's booshway, and a man did not sneak up and steal
his boss's wife while the boss wasn't looking. Not even an Indian
wife. Indian women were as desirable as ary white woman.
More. A white woman was certainly not for the life of a Rocky
Mountain trapper, for she would not live in a tepee, work her
hands off to keep a trapper warmed and fed and contented. A
trapper had the sense to know it. The sense, too, to appreciate a
good squaw.

Thinking of Isobel depressed Joe and he tried to put her out of
his mind now; to forget how he had named her Mountain
Lamb, had given her fine horses, fine cloth, and all the fufur-
row a squaw could want, and been proud as hell of her. He'd
waited, seeing how Sublette suffered from an injured leg, until
Milt guessed he would have to go back to the settlements for an
amputation. Joe was not a patient man but he actually did wait
until it seemed the head of the American Fur Company would
never return, then he had moved his possibles into Mountain
Lamb's lodge. She needed protection, didn't she? And so did
Milt's baby. Joe had played the gallant and kept the Snake
woman happy. But hell, somewhere he had failed, for Mountain
Lamb was killed. Joe's lodge was left forlorn.

Now wind drove harder, and half blinded by snow that fell
thick as puffed wool Joe left the stream, left timber, and
glimpsed dimly the vast white distance he would have to cover
to reach his camp. He wondered what day of the week it was,
and remembered the sunny Sundays when his stepmother had
made him read the family Bible that teetered on its polished oak
rack. That made him think of Narcissa Whitman, and about
her God. Now Mrs. Whitman was one missionary he could shout
about. He had come across the party of Whitmans and Spaldings,
talked to them all, but Narcissa was the one who had impressed
him. He thought briefly of something she had said—"Mr. Meek,

you should farm in Oregon"—and less briefly about the kettle
of liquor he wished for this minute. Narcissa's Bible and the
kettle shared his mind and Joe was about to get an idea out of
the wind and snow, or—he wondered—out of her Bible?

If he intended to get himself a wife he knew the girl he
wanted, knew that Chief Kowesote, her father, was always
wanting a preacher to talk to his tribe. Joe lifted his face to the
snow and laughed out loud. He would learn to preach to those
Nez Percés! "Joe Meek!" he shouted. "Whar you been all this
time?" and his words were cut off in the sharp wind. The more
he mulled it the better his idea seemed. He hadn't read and
argued, sat all night in sessions of the Rocky Mountain College to
no avail. Time was when those sessions kept trappers' winter
nights alive, and he had found some wildly interesting things in
the Bible. I could preach, he decided now, I could preach stuff
that would hit old Kowesote like a arrer, then I could go to him
and ask for the sister of Newell's wife. So he grinned, bent harder
into the wind while he pictured Dr. Whitman at Waiilatpu
Mission and tried to think how the doctor went about saving the
soul of an Injun. No reason why I cain't best Doc Whitman at
his own job, Joe told himself, and when he reached camp he
went straight to Robert Newell.

"I got a idee, Doc. That sister of your wife's is just what I
need now, and I'm about to ask old Kowesote for her. Think I
got ary chance of his agreein'?"

Newell chuckled. He was a wiry, wary man, too, and now the
rugged lines in his face cut deeper. "Not if he believes what the
missionaries have been telling him. Not if they've made any impression on the Nez Percés about many wives and damnation,"
Newell said. "Remember, Joe, you already have one squaw
somewhere among the Nez Percés. Don't expect Kowesote to
forget that."

But Joe had just had a goodly potion from his friend's kettle,
he felt warmed and optimistic. "Wall, she up and left me, didn't
she? Like ary white woman she went home to her folks. Took
my own baby, too. The fact I've lost two wives is no sign I ort
not to have another." He stretched his six feet two its length,

laughed. "If it's preaching Kowesote wants I can do the best damn preaching ever heered." Then he went to talk to Kowesote.

The chief was not surprised to be informed that Joe was a preacher. After all, he was trapper, warrior, hunter, why not preacher? That night Kowesote called his people together to listen while Joe preached a very creditable sermon. It was so enthusiastic a sermon that Meek almost believed it himself. Then he approached Kowesote without ceremony and told the chief that a wife would be very good and proper pay for his preaching.

Surprised, Kowesote drew himself up. "Your missionaries teach that no man can have two wives if Christian. Divorce a bad thing. Many Nez Percés have given up many wives. It is well known that Joe Meek has a wife somewhere among the Nez Percés."

Joe thought fast. Maybe he should admit the white man's weaknesses. "In the white settlements," he said, "if a wife deserts her man he can take another."

Kowesote's back was stiff as a gun barrel. "Meek will risk hellfire. Kowesote cannot allow that with a friend."

Well, truth had not worked. It often didn't, Joe thought, and tried again. "The white man's Holy Book tells of many men, important chiefs, having many wives."

Kowesote's black eyes glittered. "Then why do Dr. Whitman and missionary Spalding say our men must put away many wives?"

Joe was silenced. Why, indeed? An Indian needed many wives. And right now Joe needed a keeper for his lodge, someone to roast the deer meat, someone to share his bed. But Kowesote had turned on a proud heel and left him and Joe would have to think of something better.

That night he got out a Bible, turned to the Old Testament. Narcissa Whitman said that the Bible never failed a man and it had better not fail him now. So he read about Solomon, about the seven hundred wives, the princesses, and the three hundred concubines. Delighted, and reading on, he discovered that Solomon had been punished for his fun. Joe knew he must be very careful not to include the punishment in his recital to Kowesote.

For days he bothered the chief with Bible story on Bible story, called upon his friends to vouch for their truth. The Nez Percés chief was weakening and Joe knew it; the surrender did not surprise him.

"Then owning many wives is not the sin the missionaries say?"

Joe touched the Book tenderly. "So saith the Word."

"You may choose one of my daughters," Kowesote said, and Joe pointed to the handsome young sister of Newell's wife—she was sister, too, to the wife of another trapper, Caleb Wilkins. Three pretty sisters, three trapper friends, and Joe wondered what could be better. He led the girl to his lodge.

"You are Virginia," he told her, "for my own homeland." When the camp was ready to break up, start on the spring hunt, he went again to Kowesote. "It is customary for great white men to make many gifts to their preachers," he told the chief.

Kowesote knew when he had been outmaneuvered. In no time Joe had riches—prime beaver skins, horses, a handsome buffalo robe under which he and Virginia could sleep. The luck of Joe Meek! he crowed secretly, but he knew that a man's luck can't last forever. And his was not long in changing.

Now he had Virginia on his hands, and Milt Sublette's baby; somewhere there was that second squaw and any day now she might start acting like a white woman again, come back with her baby and expect him to husband her. No matter what was being said about no sale for beaver plew he'd better get out and show Doc Newell and Wilkins and all of them that beaver would rise and that somebody would buy. He persuaded his friend Allen to come along—they had trapped together many times, they would ride after while to the rendezvous on Green River.

Before they had set a trap they ran into scores of Indians, a war party of Blackfeet as sure as hell. Meek and Allen each found a hiding place where they could wait and see what was bilin'. A scout out after their horses discovered Allen, pulled him into the open, and while Allen screamed Blackfeet started cutting him into pieces.

Sickened and horrified, Joe could only watch, lying as still as death; and he thought, Joe Meek, you're scairt. You've never been so scairt in your life. Why don't you do something? But he couldn't do anything but lie low, shaking like an aspen and hearing the screams of the man who was his friend. Even Joe Meek, he had to admit, dared not walk into a crazed mess of Blackfeet.

When they had ended their orgy and moved on, taking Allen's rifle, evening and darkness brought a vast, lonely silence. And Joe was really ill. He knew his illness for fever; he began imagining stealthy sounds around him and knew them for imagination. *Meek, you fool!* he told himself over and over, and after a time managed to crawl into the place where he and Allen had left their horses. There was no sign of horses, and he lay sick and half crazed through the long night. By morning he was able to get on his feet and, making a search at no great distance, he found two of the four horses, dragged himself to the back of one. Half out of his mind with the horror he had seen he rode for days toward the Green River rendezvous. And as he rode there was no food to eat, no kettle to cheer him.

He cursed his luck, cursed the American Fur Company. A man got used, got into dangers, was underpaid, and then found himself without a job. It seemed the damnedest thing.

At rendezvous Bridger—even Jim Bridger—said the life of a mountain man and the life of the fur companies were ended. Joe was stubborn. "It ain't natural not to trap!" he shouted, but that season men left for Taos or Santa Fe, or for California, or for the Columbia where Hudson's Bay just might be buying furs. Meek did not guess it then but the Green River rendezvous of 1839 was the last for the American Fur Company.

Nights and frosts had flocked yellowing leaves along the stream, but no sun gilded the mountaintops. Joe looked up from the leather he was mending to appreciate the sight, stirred as always by first breath of winter, awed as always by the great shadows of the mountains that were home. He had been in those mountains eleven years now and he was not yet thirty. It didn't seem like sense to think that he might have to live another way.

Virginia came from the lodge, carrying the good ears of corn she would husk for boiling, and Joe, hunched on the ground, reached for a strong willow branch and stirred her fire. Joe was no squaw man. He treated his woman the way he would treat a white wife—well, nigh that way—and Indians taunted him when he failed to beat Virginia if they thought she needed beating. He looked up at the Indian girl in quick recognition of her presence, then went on tap-tapping at his boot. Neither spoke as Virginia began husking the corn.

At rustling of bare tree limbs beyond the tepee Joe threw aside the boot, jumped to moccasined feet, his rifle coming up with him.

"Never mind that!" A man named Craig stepped into the open and grinned at Joe. "Nice domestic scene thar, Meek." Joe's rifle lowered as Craig thumbed toward Virginia. "Tell her to git."

Her already flushed cheeks turned redder at his words, she got quickly to her feet, disappeared into the tepee.

"Set," Joe invited, settling himself again to the leather of his boot. "You've caught Joe Meek without a kettle but if you hadn't drove the woman off she'd have some victuals."

Craig squatted near the fire, picked up the willow branch, bent it in his hand to test it, then tossed it aside and pushed back his fur cap. "Winter's coming," he said laconically.

Joe drove in a wooden peg, agreed that it was. The easy quietness between them tightened. Off in the heavy timber a wolf howled and the thin air crisped its sound. Joe didn't look up but tapped against the boot mold and Craig said, "Put down the damned shoe and listen."

"My feet's nigh on the ground, Craig, and these boots I got to have afore the next trap settin'." Joe still didn't look up.

"Still a unbeliever. Or a crazy believer. It looks to me like there won't be any trap settin's, Meek."

At that Joe's head came up, his eyes narrowed. "Which-a-way you lookin', Craig?"

A log on the lowering campfire broke in two, fell, and sparks and flames highlighted the worry on Craig's face. "Ever stop to think, Joe, we cain't live the rest of our lives on bugs and roots like a Digger Injun?"

Joe's eyes twinkled. "I done it sometimes. Ridin' that ways to the Green I'd of chased a grasshopper if I'd had the strength." He jerked his head toward the lodge. "Good thing to have a woman that could if she had to. What's on your mind, Craig?"

"Doc Newell wants to powwow with you."

Meek, a rattle of wooden pegs between his teeth, said, "Hell. What does Doc want?"

"Newell's at Fort Hall," Craig said.

"Ary idee what's in his kettle?"

"Nary a idee," Craig lied.

The wolf howled again, got an answer. There was the crash of a falling tree limb, a rising in the wind, and Joe sniffed the air, took the pegs from his mouth. He looked up at the mountain peaks. "I reckon I can make it," he said.

It was two hundred and eighty miles to Fort Hall. They were hungry and thirsty miles but Joe plodded along, rifle across his arm, and everything he owned, including Virginia and the newest baby, piled on his one pony. He hunted out Newell and at sight of him stepped more lively.

"Doc! Ary other man on God's sod would never get me this far. Do I smell meat?"

Newell said, "Antelope Joe, since you're always hungry."

"Hungry? Starved is a puny word. How about some Taos lightnin'?"

"No lightning until you've had your supper. Maybe not then. We've got business to talk about." He was filling a tin plate but Joe took it from him.

"Wait until I take this to the woman. She'd relish a hunk of meat." And he carried food to the girl busy at making camp.

Newell smiled, watched Joe swagger back from his good deed.
"So help me, Meek, you don't change a bit."

"I'm hungrier than usual. I could eat a whole antelope." He
did very well at the good meat, filled his pipe with Newell's
tobacco. "Now, what's bilin' to make you bring me so far?"

"I've been thinking."

"Is that all?"

"It's time we got some sense, Joe, and quit these mountains.
Time we quit freezing and starving and working for no good
pay. Let's get on to Oregon, get land in the Willamette Valley,
and start farming."

Joe was silent, smoking hard. After a minute his eyes came up
to Newell's and he knew the light in Doc's eyes for what it was.
As sure as he breathed Doc was off to Oregon, and, horror of
horrors, to farm.

"You sure you can live like a white man, Bob?" Joe's grin
was a mask, pasted on to hide what was in his mind. Newell
could live white and decent, but could he, Joe Meek?

Newell said, "We both can. Think of the fine valley land, the
rivers, the game. We can never go back to the old places again,
Joe. You know that. In Oregon we can make good, keep our
finger in the pie to slow the Hudson's Bay Company. First thing
you know they're going to own Oregon. America's got some
mighty good men there, but she needs more of us to trap
Britain."

"I dunno, Doc. These yere mountains are home. Besides,
how'd we get there, me with no boots and a squaw and papooses
and one used-up pony?"

"Wagons."

Joe rubbed a big hand along his bearded jaw. "Say that again."

"Wagons, all the way to the Willamette Valley."

"Whose wagons?"

"Ours. Remember, Whitman got them this far. I aim to take
them on."

Joe slapped the pocket of his leather britches, brought out his
tobacco, and bit off a good-sized corner. He chewed thoughtfully while he offered it to Newell, and at Newell's refusal

tucked it back, slapped the pocket again. "Wagons on four wheels?"

"Three wagons, every one on four wheels."

Meek was quiet a long minute. Doc was right. They couldn't take their families back to the places they had come from. His eyes were steady as he made his decision. "I'll go whar you do, Newell. What suits you suits me."

"Good! You'll drive the first wagon. Think of it, Joe. The first wagon to Oregon! Caleb Wilkins will drive the second and Craig will take the third one. I'm glad you'll go, Meek. I don't think I'd go without you."

And so in September of 1840 the four loaded their Nez Percés wives and children and their possibles onto wagons and headed away from the Shining Mountains. There would be other and harder mountains ahead but Joe, driving a team of four horses and a mule, was heart high for adventure; happy as an Indian to take the trail.

If the Indian women beside their men felt fear of the white man's way in a white man's land they gave no sign, but kept silence. No matter what, a squaw did not question.

And no matter that wagons had never crossed the land between Fort Hall and the Columbia. The mountain men were not questioning either. The job could be done, it was theirs to do. From dawn to pitch dark and sometimes beyond they fought rivers, land, wheels, animals, and the approach of winter. Sweating and swearing, they pushed, dragged, lifted wagons; a man's only fear was that wheels would not hold out. Fear of Indians was as far from their thoughts as three wagons were from Oregon valleys.

The land was vast and quiet. Only the crunch of wheels and stiff whirr of winds broke its stillness, or pounding rain or hail. Stare ahead, push and strain; be tender with the animals, don't bother to be tender with the women. Our women are strong and steady, and sometimes their laughing helps the day. Joe thought the women were doing better than ever they had with their own people, and he felt proud. Proud, too, of the boy child Virginia had given him the time they'd been camped at Pierre's Hole. He had named the lad Courtney, a most white-sounding name, and the boy took to the trail like a true Indian.

Mud and rain. Wind and mud. Sagebrush. The Snake River in its deep canyon and no water to be had. Mountain men never carried water, for there had always been another spring or stream ahead. Or he could drink out of a wallow. But there were no wallows on the sagebrush land. Then sudden falls, white water. Fish and dirty Indians. But white water. Green land, too, and a man could think Oregon plumb to his boots. To his moccasins.

Riding ahead on a November day Newell saw the Columbia. It lay softly blue and racing his thought. He knew now. He knew it could be done.

They came to it where the Umatilla met it. "We've swum worse," they said, and got wagons and animals across. Before they finished the river had roiled in a strong wind, sand blew up on the far bank until the land was a wraith and a guessing. Sand. Sheets of it. Clouds of it. In a man's whiskers, in his eyes, in his shirt, in his brain. The squaws faced into it, set up tepees that blew down and had to be raised again and somehow anchored. But there was no somehow. So they kept to the wagons or sat without a fire, and said what a hell of a land. Sand! A mountain man could laugh at wind, plow through snow, put up with dirt. But not this kind of dirt that ground a man's eyelids and hid the land.

"June, now," Joe announced, "June ort to have saw us hittin' the trail." He was busy shaking sand out of the tail of his shirt. "But thar we was, foolin' 'til September."

Newell grinned. "June? Where were you in June?"

Joe thought, shook his head. "Can't say. But I know whar I war the June afore that—with old Jim Bridger chasin' Blackfeet. We got camped at the mouth of the Popo Agie and met up with some missionaries with ladies among 'em. Shawnees and Dela-wares got to war dancin' and I got kinda excited. Made out I could swaller fire." He chuckled. "I swallered so much fire in the shape of Taos lightnin' and strutted around so bad my Nez Percés squaw packed up and left. Carried off my own baby and

took the tepee. The papoose"—he jerked his head toward the
wagons—"same one out thar with my woman that ain't her ma,
was a blackeyed little beauty if I do say it. Made me mad as hell
when I come to an' found she'd left me nothin' but my kettle.
Of course that helped after a few swigs, so I up and started out to
find that woman." Meek's laugh was merry. "I found a woman,
but she war the wrong one, with her preacher husband about
dead, she told me. 'Water!' she yelped. 'Asa's dyin'!' I handed her
my kettle and she poured some lightnin' down him. He still was
tryin' to die so I told her to come on and leave him, he waren't
worth savin', but you know a woman. By histin' her aboard her
horse, quirtin' the animal some, and tellin' her and her preacher
that Injuns war right behind me comin' fast to scalp me, I got
her goin'. When I looked back Smith the preacher war improv-
ing his health remarkable. I told her he was goin' to catch up
with us and maybe pass us if we didn't hurry. In no time thar he
was, wantin' protection from the Injuns. So I had to admit I'd
lied." The men laughed, but Joe's laughter trailed off. "I found
my squaw in the next camp but she war still madder'n hell.
Said she'd still go home to her folks, and she did." He was
silent for some minutes before he discovered the two men across
were asleep. Then he turned to Newell. "Good thing she went,
so long as I got the little Helen Marr. Look at what a good wife
I got by preaching to Kowesote. Best persuading Joe Meek
ever done. Best woman, too, a man ever trapped."

Newell got to his feet, batted sand from his cap. The sand-
storm had quieted and there was thin sight of a moon over the
river. "We'll start early, Meek. Whitman's Mission's close and we
won't stay there long. Let's bed down."

Joe suddenly thought how warm it would be under blankets
with his woman close and he went, sock-footed, through the
sand to the wagon where she slept.

They drove up to the mission with a whoop, and the two
Whitmans hurried out to them. Joe was as pleased as ever at
sight of Narcissa. "Ever since you talked Oregon I ain't been
able to wait to get thar," he told her, which was far from the

truth and made Newell smile; but like always, there was no reason against a good lie if it would help. Mrs. Whitman very well guessed that he was exaggerating, and that Joe and perhaps the others had hated leaving their mountains. The truth was not just that Joe had been lonely for the old places; the truth was that the nearer he came to his new life the more qualms he felt. He'd been a fool to agree to start. He decided to admit his fears to Mrs. Whitman.

"I talk big but I'm scairt. Doc will be big stuff in Oregon, but what can I do? Farm? Wagh! My pappy worked slaves on our plantation and all I did was look on, play with the black boys. And what folks! Sometimes I miss those boys yet."

She encouraged him; told him Oregon had places for every strong, fine man and that he was strong and fine and she just knew it. She was so gentle with him and with the young Helen Marr that he begged to leave the child with her. "Bring her up your way," he said. "She ort not be brought up my way. I got two boys out thar," he confessed. "One belonged to my boosh-way Milt Sublette, that I got when he left Isobel." Seeing Narcissa's concern he added, "Milt warn't a deserter, ma'am. Got a leg hurt and wanted it off. So I got my Mountain Lamb when he went back to the settlements." Narcissa asked about Sublette. "Oh, he made it back, leg and all, but he told me I could keep her. I been uncommon lucky. This Virginia along with me for Oregon is another lamb if ever a man had one. She handed me the other boy, Courtney."

"How does Virginia feel about living in white man's land, Mr. Meek?" Narcissa's question made Joe jump.

"Hell. Damned if I know! I never asked her." Then he said please excuse him for swearing, remembered proper Virginia manners, and bent over her hand, touched it with his rough lips. He did not look back at the young Helen Marr, but bolted from the room.

As the three wagons pulled away Meek said to Newell, who rode alongside, "You think I done right, Doc?"

"Leaving the child? No doubt about it, Joe."

Feeling small comfort, Meek jerked hard on the lines and shouted at his horses, told his mule to get to blazes and start pulling.

Oregon was a real big place, but Joe felt elbowed by missionaries and preachers. There seemed to be a mission every time you looked, and people aplenty at every mission, not very many outside. At The Dalles, Newell said they had proved wagons could get to the Columbia but now they would have to leave wheels and take to boats. Any kind of boats they could rig. The brief time they spent at Hudson's Bay Company's Fort Vancouver proved one thing to Joe: it took a mountain man to put up with a missionary. John McLoughlin, at the Factor's desk, seemed to get along with them, but then McLoughlin was a fur man, too.

Robert Newell left for Oregon City and Joe, along with five other mountain men, trailed squaw and pony, babies and possibles to the Tuality Plains, nearer the Willamette River than anything he had sighted, and wetter than any wet land he had ever waded. It was Christmas Eve of 1840.

Whatever day that came was a rainy day. Rain and mud, worse than any time from Fort Hall. December in Oregon soaked a man's soul, soaked his moccasins until they parted, soaked the buffalo-hide lodges until they dripped for days after rains ceased—if rains ever ceased. Buckskin shirts stuck to backs; boiled wheat, boiled wheat, more boiled wheat, stuck in throats. There was no game. If there was Joe couldn't find it. Neighbors said there were bears, wolves, cougars; but they felt enough pity for the mountain men that they brought dried salmon—and wheat to boil!

"One more mess of this biled wheat and I'm going to bile a couple of missionaries," Joe told Caleb Wilkins. "Ary Methodist stick his head in my lodge better keep his eye peeled." But he was laughing uproariously in the next minute at thought of how a missionary would taste. "Talk about your biled wheat, I'll bet they'd need sugar!" He decided that tough as the fur men were, no man in Oregon had bigger hearts or bigger ways—not preachers, not missionaries, not farmers. For genuine all-around cussed bigness, give Joe a mountain man every time.

Now it was the second of May, 1843. Joe Meek was about to leave his place on the Tuality Plains for a meeting at Champoeg by the Willamette, and so he threw saddle to the back of his horse, looked down at the boy whose big dark eyes waited for an answer.

"The meeting is for men," Joe told his son. "No place for you."

"I could stay out of sight—"

"You could do as I say and go back to your mother."

Young Courtney frowned. "You said it would be a great thing. You said no man should miss what would happen on French Prairie. I will soon be a man."

Joe chuckled. "We're all old men today—past thirty mostly. When you are old you will help decide things, too."

"I could learn today."

Meek laughed outright, put a hand on the lad's shoulder. "You are a stubborn chip off the old Joe Meek block," he said, pride swelling his words. "When you are old, and voting, you will be an American, just as you are now. You will if we do the right thing today. Otherwise, who knows? You might be Hudson's Bay beaver, or under the thumb of England. You go tell your mother to talk hard to her sun gods today—rain gods, too, to be safe in this valley—tell her to talk hard for America. Go now."

The boy turned, ran quickly, his feet fleet as a deer's, bow and arrow clutched in a strong hand, and Meek, watching him, saw himself the day he had run away from his father's plantation, determined to catch a wagon ride to a place, any place, where he could join a pack train for the Shining Mountains. He had been some years older than Courtney, and just as stubborn. One of his Negro playmates to whom he had told his secret plan had laughed at him.

"Y'awl get yander, ain't nobody gwine let you start off be a

mountain man. You paw get his gun go hunt you an' fotch you
home. Skin you hide right off you bones, I reckon!" But his pa
had not followed. Joe had been scared, a little, but swaggering
some as soon as he had found a job with Milt and William
Sublette. He'd be a mountain man!

Now here was a thing. He and the others had asked many
times why they had ever left the sweet, high, dry Rocky
Mountains for a drowned-out place like Tuality Plains, but
this morning he knew. He eyed the shining river, trees along its
banks, some of them pretty nearly giant; the wild roses just
budding in open spots, first sun lifting the last of ghost fog
from the river, the soft blue-green Oregon sky, the close-in hills
and far purple mountains, and it was not of Christmas Eve
more than two years ago that he thought. Perhaps he would not
think of that again. Something stirred Meek to say to the
river and to the hills and to the trees, "Now, by God, I know!"
and to spur his horse toward French Prairie. Toward the thing
to be decided at Champoeg.

This was the third meeting on French Prairie, the first had
considered a form of government, for a man named Young
had died, and how should a lawless land settle his estate? No
one knew. The second had been called to set bounties on de-
structive wild animals and, dubbed the Wolf Meeting, had ordered a report of a committee for a Provisional Government
under America, a government to be taken over by the United
States at a proper time. Appointment of such a committee had
been more or less slipped in under wolf's clothing, some said;
French Canadians and Hudson's Bay Company opposed the
whole thing and John McLoughlin would see that they were
there in numbers today. Joe could smell battle miles before he
rode in, tethered his horse.

Newell was already there, Caleb Wilkins was there; some
of the fur men were in summer garb of blue shirt and leather
belt with knife and powder horn slung from it, but Joe still
wore buckskins minus, however, his winter-going buffalo-hide
shoes. He could count a few high silk hats, some beaver ones,

frock coats, and boots that had a shine. Farmers were there in
hickory shirts; men from the missions wore Sunday garb. The
coffee had already begun to smell good, and tables had been set
under the trees, women in big aprons and bright sunbonnets
moved about in the shade of maples and alders and firs. Other
times food had seemed more important to Meek than business,
but today was different and he moved about among the men,
his laugh big and his banter friendly. He felt the need to bring
votes to his side.

"Now you, Matthieu! And Lucier! You vote right. Don't fail
America!"

Etienne Lucier and Francis Matthieu were not quite sure.
Both were old-timers with Hudson's Bay, but Matthieu had left
it in bad humor. Just the same he was French Canadian, so was
Lucier, and whose land, actually, should this be?

Lucier argued. "America's taxes—there are always taxes."

Meek slapped Lucier's shoulder and laughed. "Hell, man, I
never paid one cent of taxes in my whole life. You can forget
taxes!"

"That's true," Matthieu said.

"He owns land?"

"*Oui!* It grows crops. I've seen it—"

"Well—"

Joe thought he could move on. He sought out others. "How
does it look?"

"McLoughlin's got his trappers thick as flies around here,"
they told Joe. "All cocky, too, sure Hudson's Bay will rule
the roost like always. And you know McLoughlin!"

Joe did. He had spent more days than he could count at the
Company's fort, liking the food, liking the man who ruled it
and the tight control McLoughlin exercised over obstreperous
Indians, over any man who hindered the orderly Hudson's Bay
regime; admiring the aid the good doctor was always ready
to give settlers. But there were things he did not like: the way
McLoughlin loaned cattle and horses to farmers, then called
them in, never agreeing to sell as much as one calf to a family
in need, one cow, one ox, to a man needing to own, not borrow.

McLoughlin, taller even than Joe Meek, looked and was a really great man, commanding other men, nodding his white-maned head or refusing to nod over requests, over decisions; demanding work from every man, even Joe. "Mr. Joe, Mr. Joe," he had said on a day when Meek had teased him with glory stories about Indians, "you must stop killing Indians and go to work!" It had taken quite a long time for McLoughlin to agree to loan Joe the wherewithal for plowing.

Joe said now, "I recollect McLoughlin all right. We best keep our eyes open."

And while they kept eyes open the report was read. There was excitement, noisy talk. The peace of the prairie was no longer peace and Meek circled around, encouraging the clamor.

Someone shouted, "Mr. Chairman! Let's not wait. We can set up a government among ourselves."

There was louder argument and Father Blanchette cautioned against hurry. "The Hudson's Bay Company has always been the one to settle our questions—"

"In their own damned way!" a loud voice shouted.

"Order! Order!" the chairman cried. But there was no sign of order. As if to remind these men that there was more to this than a battle of uncalled-for swearwords the chairman waited, himself quiet, eyes here and there over the hundred and two. Slowly the talk died down, began again.

Meek thought, There's the way that Cayuse Injun told me out thar on the road—"Injuns have lost faith in the white man and the white man has lost faith in McLoughlin; missionaries ain't helped the Indians with their prayers, ain't made 'em any richer, just took away their wives. And white men are fighting among themselves over a very foolish question such as who should rule Oregon." The Cayuse had answered the question for Joe. "The Indian. My people of course. It is his country." Joe had thought then that it looked as if any minute Oregon Country might explode. And here it was, exploding.

Finally the argument ended and the chairman asked, "Shall the chair put the question?"

"Question!"

"Hell, yes!"

"Question! Question!"

"Gentlemen, the question is called for. Those in favor say 'Aye.'"

There was a roaring shout of "Aye!"

"Contrary?"

Another roar. "No!"

Both sides were so sure. The chairman called for a show of hands. Hands showed. The Americans groaned. It looked as if they had lost, and they could not believe it.

Someone called, "Divide! Divide!"

This moment was Joe Meek's. This was his hour, the hour in which history would wrap him, a mountain man, toss him sky-high in its blanket of fame. He took long strides to one side.

"Who's for a divide?" he called out, and the echo of it crossed the river to the hills. "Those for the report follow me!"

They followed, forty-nine of them, but two, Lucier and Matthieu stood close together whispering. Lucier gestured. That Lucier, with his talk of taxes—Joe held his breath. What if Lucier went one way, Matthieu the other?

A robin trilled somewhere nearby. Matthieu turned, and Lucier turned, walked beside him to join Meek.

Joe's heart swelled. This was America then! This—and he saw the land stretching through mountains, beyond the Tetons, the Black Hills, plumb to the Atlantic—and Virginia! It was all one now. It was America's and he knew every foot of it.

Some things Joe Meek did not know: that in an hour he would be elected High Sheriff for the Provisional Government of Oregon and that one day he would go from here to Washington to ask his cousin, President Polk, for ary reason why his Congress should not quit sawing on the reins and give Oregon her statehood.

Joe Meek had been one of the proud ones who helped open the West and he was as content this moment at Champoeg as he would ever be.

Where the Wind Blows Free

BY BILL GULICK

The Conestoga wagon and a hundred other varieties of "prairie schooner" made early appearance on the Western scene. In one brief decade they carried overland more passengers and goods than all the shipping arriving in the port of San Francisco prior to the Civil War. However, contrary to general supposition, they were not variations of the big, heavy, broad-tired freighters which came into use on the graded surfaces of such highways as the National Road and later on the arid, generally level traces of the Santa Fe and Pike's Peak trails. These were too cumbersome, too punishing to draft stock and drivers, for the rivers and grades and gumbo of the "highways" to the Pacific. The prairie schooner evolved by trial, error, and ingenuity from the settlers' own much lighter and more simply constructed farm wagons. Hardware was reduced to a minimum. Reaches were simplified to make replacement possible with a trailside sapling, cut to size. Boxes grew narrower and deeper, higher at front and rear—indeed quite boatlike—and planking came to be fitted in ship style to be water-tight against interminable crossings of rivers and streams. The best were virtually indestructable and many survived to give a generation of service in the valley of the Willamette and the gulches of the Mother Lode. But stout as they were, survival of men and wagons alike rested solely in the hands of the train "captains" who guided them— part scout, part judge, part counselor, and often tyrants, independent and arrogant, fighting a hostile land for day wages with total responsibility for as many as a hundred wagons and all they contained on their shoulders alone. —T.W.B.

WHEN the stranger rode into camp, Freda Eklunds was down on her knees before a pan of hot, soapy water, washing dishes. The dry June wind coming off the sage-covered desert beyond Fort Bridger had loosened a strand of her braided yellow hair, and, in exasperation, she had made a hasty back-hand pass at it, succeeding only in getting suds in her right eye. With a cry of dismay, she lifted her apron, wiped the strong lye soap from the offended eye, and then looked up through a misty film as the stranger swung off his horse.

"'Scuse me, ma'am. This the Wagner outfit?"

"Yes."

"Whar'll I find Lucius Wagner?"

"Over there," she answered, started to point, then, as a flood of tears came again, tried to stem them with her apron.

"Somethin' troublin' you?" the man said, concerned.

"Soap. Just soap."

As her vision cleared, she saw that he was tall, lean, and dark, wore ragged, greasy buckskins, and, despite his self-assured air, appeared to be only a few years older than she. His black eyes twinkled.

"Glad to hear that. Thought I'd busted in on a private cry."

Resuming her chore with an angry toss of her head, she covertly watched him lead his horse toward the wagon in whose shade the Wagner family was resting. Mr. Wagner, a hearty, red-faced man in his early fifties, was napping. Mrs. Wagner, a solid woman with a firm chin and disposition to match, was making sure that her six children—who ranged in age from nine to sixteen—were concentrating on their books to make up for the schoolwork they were missing. *I should have warned him that the Wagners dislike being disturbed at this hour,* Freda mused. *Well, he'll learn that soon enough.*

"Howdy, ma'am. I'm Jeff Clayton. Jim Bridger sent me over—"

"If you wish to see my husband," Mrs. Wagner cut in, "he cannot be disturbed. Come back later."

Mr. Wagner opened his eyes. "It is all right, Mama. I am awake. What do you want, Mr. Clayton?"

"Jim says you're lookin' for a guide to take you through to Oregon."

"We are."

"Wal, that's my business."

"You know the way?"

"Blindfolded."

Vigorously scrubbing a plate, Freda marveled that an uncouth, ignorant, poorly dressed man such as this one should approach the Wagners and ask for a job so casually. The Wagners were rich, socially important people of the best Pennsylvania Dutch stock. Back in Philadelphia, Mr. Wagner had owned a prosperous brewery, lived in a fine house, and circulated with gentlemen of means. Yet Jeff Clayton dared interrupt Mr. Wagner's nap and stand in Mrs. Wagner's presence without even doing her the courtesy of removing his hat. Mr. Wagner, who always conferred with his wife on important decisions, glanced at her questioningly.

"What do you think, Mama?"

Her sharp eyes surveyed the young man. "How much pay do you ask?"

"Four dollars a day."

"Two is plenty."

"Four, ma'am. Take it or leave it."

Freda stifled a gasp. Mrs. Wagner would send him packing, of course. Such insolence from a hired servant could not be tolerated! True, the guide that had brought the twelve wagons in the train this far had quit a week ago and headed for the California gold fields. Guides did seem to be a necessity in this country and the enforced layover was making everyone restless. All the same, she was certain what Mrs. Wagner would say. She felt sorry for Jeff Clayton, despite his arrogance, for he looked like he badly needed the job.

Mrs. Wagner's eyes snapped. "Three. That is all we will pay."

Jeff Clayton turned to his horse. "Oregon lies due west. Good luck."

There was a murmur of discontent from the emigrant families that had gathered around. Mr. Wagner scowled, conferred in whispers with his wife, then said, "Wait. We will pay you four dollars. But only on our terms."

The black eyes were amused. "And what might they be?"

"That you do not quit us whenever you feel like it, as the other guide did. That you take us safely through to Oregon City before you receive one dollar of your pay."

"Fair enough." Swinging into the saddle, he gave the Wagners an informal salute. "Now if you'll excuse me I got some business to do at the fort. See you in the mornin'."

Because she knew what it was like to be without money, a job, or friends, Freda was glad that Jeff Clayton had found work despite his lack of manners. She determined to teach him the Wagners' ways so that he would not offend them. Being far too timid to speak directly to a man she had barely met, she found an errand to do at the fort that afternoon and said her piece haltingly to Jim Bridger, whom she knew to be a kindly, understanding man. When she was done, he gave her a seaching look.

"Kind of took to Jeff, didn't you?"

"Oh, no!" she said hastily, coloring. "It is just that I want to help him."

"He'll be obliged, ma'am."

Freda had cooked and served the Wagners their breakfast, next morning, when Jeff Clayton came nonchalantly riding into camp. One horrified look told Freda her well-meant advice had been completely ignored. He had not trimmed his hair, bathed, shaved, or changed his filthy buckskins, as she had told Bridger he must do. His eyes were bleary; he complained of an aching head and a stomach full of butterflies; he scorned the good breakfast she had kept warm for him; he drank three cups of coffee, but said it was too weak; and then, when she indignantly refused his suggestion that she snitch a pint of "old man Wagner's whisky" and sneak it to him as an eye-opener, he stalked off muttering profanely that if he'd knowed this was going to be a dry drive damned if he'd have hired on.

Freda was so angry she hoped the Wagners would fire him.

But both Mr. and Mrs. Wagner were too preoccupied to notice his condition and the wagons moved out in good order. Under his apparently casual guidance, they made good time across the high, sage-covered plains lying west of Fort Bridger, struck Bear River and followed its lush valley northwesterly, left it where the river swung south, and wound without incident through the rough, lava-strewn country beyond. Reaching the juncture of the Portneuf with the Snake, two weeks later, Freda heard Jeff tell Mr. Wagner that it would be wise to camp here for a few days, readying the wagons and resting the oxen for the tough going of the Snake River Desert ahead.

After breakfast, next morning, Mrs. Wagner said, "When you have finished the dishes, Freda, the clothes you will wash. You will need the big tub, wood for the fire, and lots of hot water."

"Yes, Mrs. Wagner."

Hurrying through the dishes, Freda put them away, went over to one of the wagons, and struggled to lift down the big wooden tub resting on the high tailgate. It proved stubborn to move. She heard Jeff, who was lying on one elbow near the fire, say to Mr. Wagner, "That's a heavy tub, Lucius."

"Yes," Mr. Wagner agreed. "It is a good, solid tub." He raised his voice. "Your shoulder you should put under it, Freda."

Freda flushed. "Yes, Mr. Wagner."

She heard Jeff give a grunt of disgust. He rose, crossed to the wagon, and lifted the tub to the ground for her. She thanked him with her eyes, turned, and hastily picked up bucket and ax. To her amazement he snatched them roughly out of her hands. "No need for you to do that with all these husky kids standin' around. Adolph, fetch some water. Ludwig, go chop some firewood. Hustle, now!"

Freda whispered urgently, "Jeff, please!"

Mrs. Wagner's eyes shot fire. "You will give no orders to my children, Mr. Clayton."

"Wal, they wa'n't doin' nothin', so I thought—"

"That is servant's work. Freda!"

"Yes, Mrs. Wagner! I go!"

"You wish she should have help, Mr. Clayton?" Mrs. Wagner said with an icy smile. "Very well. You help her."

Freda saw Jeff's jaw drop. "Me? You're orderin' me to carry water and wood like an Injun squaw?"

Panic-stricken, Freda took bucket and ax out of his hands and ran toward the river. Catching up with her, he grabbed her arm, stopped her, and said angrily, "Now, what'd you go and do that for?"

"Please, Jeff, you must not argue with her! She will become very angry!"

"That's no skin off my nose."

"You will lose your job! Four dollars a day is a great deal of money!"

She saw his black eyes flicker, angry at first, then amused, then thoughtful. "How much are they payin' you?"

"Oh, I am paid nothing. I am indentured servant."

"You mean to tell me you work for free?"

"They give me my meals and bed."

Jeff gave a snort of derision. "They do that much for their oxen. How come you put up with it?"

As he cut wood and carried water for her, she told him. Back in Sweden, her homeland, her father had been a gunsmith, and the tales he had read about Oregon had fascinated him. A year ago he had brought his family to America, determined to make his future in that bright new land; but shortly after the family reached Philadelphia smallpox had taken everyone except Freda. She had been barely eighteen, homeless, and frightened. With no money, no relatives or friends in this country and a hazy notion that Oregon was a place where all dreams came true, she had found the Wagners planning to emigrate there and indentured herself to them as a servant.

"For how long?" Jeff asked quietly.

"Five years."

"Then what'll you do?"

Shyly she lowered her eyes, her voice warm and full of hope.

"If I am a good servant, perhaps when my time is up they will give me a little dowry. Then I can find a husband."

"What the devil's a dowry?"

She stared at him in amazement. "You do not know? Why, it is what every girl must have before she can get married!"

His eyes surveyed her from head to toe. "'Pears to me you've already got all a gal needs—and then some."

"Oh, Jeff, do not joke! A dowry is a gift to her husband—a cow, a little house, a piece of land, a sum of money."

"You mean to tell me the fella gets *paid* to marry her?"

"It is not pay. It is a start for married life. How else can a young couple get a start for married life?"

He rubbed his chin, thinking that over. "Why, it's plumb easy. If a fella's got any gumption at all, he shakes the dust of his folks' farm off his boots, takes his gun, his horse and his ax, and travels west till he finds a piece of land that suits his eye—"

"Who gives him this gun, this horse, this ax?"

"Nobody. He buys 'em."

"Where does he get the money?"

"Wal, his arms ain't broke, are they?"

Puzzled, she gazed at him. "What do you mean?"

"Jest that a little money ain't hard to come by if he ain't scared of work. He can take a job—"

"Why should he? His folks have land, yes? Why does he not stay home and work there?"

Her innocent questions appeared to irritate him. "You don't get the idea at all. Take me, for instance. My folks had a good farm back in Ohio but we had a big family and my foot took to itchin'. So I said the hell with farmin', came west, and started trappin' beaver—"

"You were poaching?"

"Huh?"

"Who did the beaver belong to? Who gave you permission to trap them?"

Before he could answer, Katrina and Peter, the youngest of the Wagner children, came running up and told Freda Mama was wondering when she was going to start the washing. Jeff

gave them a message to carry back to their mama that made
Freda cover her ears with her hands; then, as he leaned over and
picked up an armload of wood, he grunted, "You got a lot to
learn about this country, young lady. Like it or not, I'm going to
be your teacher."

"And you," she said primly, picking up the bucket of water,
"have much to learn about manners. Perhaps it will be I who
shall teach you!"

That settled, they went back to camp.

Jeff meant well, Freda knew, but the sad truth was he was
short on patience. He was always preaching what a great thing
it was to be free, but when she'd say: "Free from what?" he'd
blow up and ask her what fool system of government had she
been raised under, anyway? His bluntness hurt her; she would
quit speaking to him; he'd come to her and apologize, saying
he hadn't meant it personal, that it was he who was stupid, not
her, and why didn't she please learn him some manners?

She tried. For instance, she said, it was very rude of him to
stare blankly off into space, pretending to be deaf and dumb,
when Mrs. Wagner asked him to do some task. He disagreed. Just
because he lent Freda a hand when her chores got too heavy
for her seemed to give Mrs. Wagner the notion he'd jump when
she said frog. But damned if he would. Only way of curing Mrs.
Wagner of ordering him around was by giving her the deaf-and-
dumb Injun treatment.

"But must you make her so angry?"

"I ain't her personal servant."

"Her husband pays your salary."

"As a guide, that's all."

"But if you displease her, she will make her husband discharge
you. Then what will you do?"

"Wal, I won't starve, you can bet on that."

"How can you be sure? Who would take care of you?"

He threw back his head and laughed. "Hell, gal, 'long as a
man's got his health, a gun, and a lick of sense, he can't possibly

starve in this country. Beaver, buffalo, antelope, deer—why, they're all free for the takin'. So is the land."

"What land?"

"Most all of it." His dark eyes sobered. "Why, honey," he boasted, "if I had a mind to I could claim three hundred and twenty acres in Oregon. If I had me a wife, I could claim a whole square mile. After I'd lived on it long enough to prove I intended to stay, the government would give me title to it free and clear. I could cut down trees, build a house, farm, raise cattle, or do anything else I was man enough to do, without asking leave of nobody."

She thought that over. "How much land could Mr. Wagner claim?"

"The same as me, no more."

That, she guessed, was an outright lie. But she let him think she believed it, just to keep the peace.

One evening in early September the wagons made camp in a grassy valley on the western slope of a range of mountains Jeff said were the Blues. When Freda had finished her chores he took her for a walk. In the twilight they stopped and sat down on a rock. As Jeff filled his pipe Freda gestured into the purpling distance.

"This is Oregon?"

"Eastern edge of it, yeah."

"Where is the free land?"

"All over."

"Here—right here?"

"Far as I can see, nobody's claimed this valley yet."

She sat quite still, her eyes taking in the wide, grass-covered meadow below and the sparkling stream wandering across it. The soil looked deep, rich, and free from stones, and, overlooking the valley, tall, straight pine and hemlock trees, much like those of her own country, covered the higher slopes as far as her eyes could see. Her voice filled with awe.

"Jeff . . ."

"Yeah?"

"You could take a square mile of this valley for yourself?"

"Sure—if I had a wife."

"Why don't you?"

He puffed silently on his pipe for a time. "Wal, I guess I ain't ready to settle down yet. I mean, I'd have to find the right sort of gal. . . ."

"Don't you want a wife?"

"Someday . . ."

"Where will you look for her, Jeff?"

"Ain't give that much thought."

She averted her eyes. "I hope you fine one with a handsome dowry."

"Why would I want one with a dowry? My arms ain't broke."

She looked at him. "You have said that before. I do not understand what it means."

"It means I've got some pride. I'm able to put clothes on her back, food in her mouth, and a roof over her head. Long as she had some git-up-and-go to her, I wouldn't care if she didn't have a dime."

Despite her efforts to master the English language, there were still occasional phrases Jeff used that Freda failed utterly to comprehend. This was one. Before she could ask him to explain it to her, Mrs. Wagner called from camp, "Freda! Freda, come here at once!"

Hastily Freda got up and went; but from the look Jeff gave her she gathered that this wasn't the kind of git-up-and-go he'd meant.

There was the damp chill of early autumn in the air when the wagon train made camp at The Dalles, some days later. Westward, Freda could see tall mountains looming, slashed by a wide, rapids-filled river. She heard Jeff say to Mr. Wagner, "We got a choice to make here, Lucius. Oregon City lies a hundred miles west, beyond the Cascades yonder. But there's two routes we can take."

"Which is easiest?"

"They're both mean. We can take the wagons apart and raft 'em through the Gorge. Or we can cross the mountains on Bar-

low's Toll Road, which is jest one notch better'n no road at all.
If we stick to the river, we'll get mighty wet. If we cross the
mountains, we'll have some stiff climbin' to do."

"You are the guide, Mama says. It is for you to decide."

"Wal, I'd rather climb than swim."

Mr. Wagner smiled and clapped Jeff on the back. Freda was
pleased to hear him say, "You have been a good guide, Jeff.
Tonight we will have a little party to celebrate the nearing
end of our journey."

It was a nice party, Freda mused as she watched the couples
dancing and heard the men chatting jovially around the whisky
barrel which Mr. Wagner had set out despite his wife's frown
of protest. Eying Jeff with concern, she hoped he would remember his place and not drink too much, for with things going
so well between him and Mr. Wagner she had begun to enter-
tain a secret dream. Mr. Wagner would be an important man
in Oregon, no doubt about that. If Jeff chose to settle down, perhaps Mr. Wagner would give him a job in his brewery. If
Jeff worked hard, was sober, industrious, and thrifty, then by
the time Freda's five years were up . . .

She sighed in dismay. Urged on by the menfolk, Jeff had
jumped into the center of the firelit circle and was doing a wild
Indian war dance. That overcame whatever inhibitions he
may have had against sociable dancing and he snatched her to
her feet and gave her a whirl that left her breathless. Well aware
of what Mrs. Wagner's attitude would be toward having a servant girl join the party uninvited, Freda tore loose from him,
but Jeff, unperturbed, grabbed first one, then another of the
ladies and cavorted with them. To Freda's horror, one of his
partners was Mrs. Wagner, which caused whoops of laughter
from the onlookers. What Mrs. Wagner thought of that, Freda
had no chance to observe, for now Mr. Wagner, carried away
by the spirit—or spirits—of the evening, jubilantly seized Freda
and danced with her.

That surely must have shocked Mrs. Wagner, Freda thought,
panic-striken. But Mr. Wagner wasn't done yet. As the dance

ended he picked Freda up, whirled her around until her skirts flew, and then gave her a juicy, alcoholic kiss square on the lips.

Mrs. Wagner broke loose from Jeff's grasp and crossed the circle. With a cry of outrage, she slapped Freda hard, jerked her husband around, planted an openhanded blow against his startled face, then, her face like a thundercloud, read the riot act to all present.

"Enough! Enough of this disgusting drinking, dancing, and kissing! No more will I stand for!"

The party ended. Her face aflame, Freda stared down at her shoe tips. "I am sorry, Mrs. Wagner. So sorry!"

In the sudden silence Jeff strode to her side, put his arm around her quivering shoulders, and said hotly, "What's to be sorry for? No harm was intended nor done. If you want my opinion, Mrs. Wagner—"

"Your opinion you will keep to yourself, Mr. Clayton! You are a paid servant, no more!"

"Wal, that's your notion," Jeff said, the anger in his voice so deep it frightened Freda. "But mine happens to be a sight different. Any old time you start slappin' Freda around—"

"Jeff!" Freda begged, frantically squeezing his arm. "Be still! Please be still!"

He gave her a long, searching look. Then he turned abruptly on his heel and stalked off into the dark.

It took two weeks to make the mountain crossing. In all that wearying time Jeff walked not once with Freda of evenings. Nor did he associate with or speak to the Wagners except in the strict line of the business at hand. He was angry, she knew, and he was hurt. That he could be hurt touched her deeply; that she had hurt him while he was trying to protect her and she was trying to protect him made it all the worse.

The last hill which they must descend was so steep the only way to get a wagon down was to tie a log behind its rear wheels as a drag, lock the wheels, and ease the vehicle downgrade by means of ropes belayed around the trunk of a thick fir on the height. Ordering the women and children to stand clear, Jeff supervised the men in the slow, hard, backbreaking work with a skill that made Freda marvel at his ingenuity. He got all but the last of the wagons to the bottom of the hill without incident. Then, as it inched along, halfway down, a frayed rope broke, and the wagon went tumbling end over end down the slope, landing on an immense rock that splintered it into kindling wood.

Jeff took it calmly. After making sure no one had been injured, he said to Mr. Wagner, "That's the first one we've lost. We're lucky, Lucius."

"Lucky?" Mr. Wagner stormed. "It was *my* wagon!"

"Wal, you started west with two and you've still got one left. Outside of the wagon itself and a barrel of busted dishes, there's no damage done."

Down on her knees in the wreckage, Mrs. Wagner let out a frenzied howl. "Lucius! Those dishes were my Sunday-best china!"

The glint in Jeff's eyes warned Freda that he had been pushed almost as far as he would go. But Mrs. Wagner failed to see it. Lighting into him, she tongue-lashed him for five solid minutes before she paused for breath. He didn't interrupt, but his eyes got darker and darker. When Mrs. Wagner was done, he looked at her husband.

"Know what I'd do with that mouthy squaw of yours if she was mine?"

"Lucius!" Mrs. Wagner screamed. "Did you hear what he called me?"

"I'd cut me a length of sapling, like so," Jeff said, measuring off the proper length with his hands. "Then I'd lay it onto her good and proper. Makes 'em quit every time."

Freda saw Mr. Wagner's face turn red, then white. She saw him gaze vacantly off into the forest, as if looking for something. Then, recovering himself, he exploded: "You are discharged, Mr. Clayton!"

"You don't have to fire me. I quit." He pointed west. "The road's clear and easy the rest of the way. You can't miss it. Give me my pay and I'll be riding."

Trembling with anger, Mr. Wagner fished his purse out of his pocket. "I'll be happy to. How much do we owe you?"

"Ninety days I've put up with you. That's three hundred and sixty dollars, way I figger."

"Wait, Papa!" Mrs. Wagner said, a calculating gleam coming into her eyes. "Remember the bargain? No pay was he to get until safely we arrived in Oregon City. We have not arrived. Yet he quits. With his own mouth he said it. So no pay do we owe him."

"You are right, Mama." Mr. Wagner smiled at Jeff. "That was the bargain."

Freda gasped, for without a word Jeff had strode over to his horse, got his rifle, and turned around. As he started to speak, an involuntary movement on her part drew his eyes to her. He stared at her long and hard. She returned his gaze, silently imploring him to do nothing he might later regret. She saw his black eyes flicker with sudden decision.

"Lucius," he said quietly, "how much is Freda worth to you?"

Mr. Wagner stared at him blankly. "Freda? You ask how much she is worth?"

"Yeah. That indentured-servant guff don't shine out here. If she had the gumption, she could take her freedom. But she won't. She's scared to. So I'll buy it for her. I'm askin' you to make a choice, Lucius—give me my pay in cash or give me Freda. You got jest ten seconds to make up your mind."

Mr. Wagner looked uncertainly at his wife. "Mama—?"

"Servant girls we can get any day," Mrs. Wagner said scornfully. "Cash money is hard to come by. Give her to him."

"You heard that, Freda?" Jeff said.

"Yes."

"Go pack your things. I'll take you to Oregon City."

She did not move. "And after that?"

"Why, that's up to you, I reckon," he said irritably. "I got no use for a servant. But you'll have your freedom."

"What will I do with it?"

Jeff stared at her. "Do you mean to tell me you won't take it?"

"Not this way. Not by having you buy it."

"Wal, what difference does it make how you get it," he demanded, "jest so long as you're free?"

"A great difference—to me."

Anger flared in his face. She wanted desperately to cry out: *Please, Jeff—please understand!* but no words came. With a grunt of disgust, he turned and picked up his horse's trailing reins, jammed his left foot into the stirrup and roared, "Wal, like it or not, you're free! Your debt to me is paid, Lucius. I'm headin' back to Fort Bridger to give old Jim a piece of my mind for ever tellin' me herdin' pilgrims beats trappin' beaver. But you let Freda alone, you hear me, 'cause if I ever get word you or your wife are pesterin' her—!"

"Jeff!" Freda cried, running toward him. "You must understand why I said what I did! You can't go this way!"

"Watch me! Jest watch me! I'm goin' back to the mountains, I am, and find me an Injun squaw—"

A horse always senses the mood its master is in, Jeff had once told Freda; thus, the wise man controls his temper when approaching his mount. But right now he was so mad he threw wisdom to the winds. Just as he swung his right leg over the horse's back, that usually calm-natured beast snorted, stuck his head between his forelegs, and humped his body violently. Freda screamed as she saw Jeff sail through the air, do a slow half-turn, then pile into the ground with a jarring thump.

She ran to him and helped him sit up. "Jeff! Are you hurt?"

He stared down at his limp right arm. "Busted a wing, seems like."

"Just what you deserve," Mrs. Wagner said unsympathetically. "Come, Lucius."

As the Wagners moved toward their wagon, Freda started to protest, but Jeff muttered, "Let 'em go. I'll make out. Now if you'll just fix up my arm—"

But Freda had a much more urgent matter on her mind. Getting to her feet, she called in a clear, firm voice—not at all a servant's voice, "Mr. Wagner!"

Surprised at her tone, he paused. "Yes?"

"Before you go, there are three things I want of you."

Amused, he gazed at her. "And what are they?"

"First, my clothes."

"You may have them."

"And my freedom."

"That you have already. Didn't you hear the agreement we made with Mr. Clayton?"

"I heard it, yes. But I am not a horse or cow to be sold in the marketplace. I am taking my freedom for myself. Do you understand?"

He shrugged impatiently. "Very well, Freda. You have it. Why argue how you are getting it?"

"Because," Freda said quietly, "if I am taking my freedom for myself, if no one is buying it for me, you still owe Jeff three hundred and sixty dollars. And before you leave, I insist you pay it."

Mr. Wagner laughed heartily. "Insist all you like, my dear. It will do you no good." His face darkened. "Now get your clothes and let us go."

Freda quite lost her temper. Stooping, she picked up Jeff's rifle, leveled it, and cocked it. "The money, Mr. Wagner—I want it right now."

Mr. Wagner reached for his purse. . . .

After the preacher in Oregon City had married them, Jeff said the sensible thing to do was wait till spring before they filed a homestead claim on that valley in eastern Oregon. By then, he said, his arm would be healed and he'd be up to doing heavy farm work.

Freda just smiled and said, "No, we need not wait. Let us go at once—tomorrow."

"But, Freda, all that work—"

"Who's afraid of work?" she murmured as she kissed him. "We're both free now, aren't we? And *my* arms aren't broke."

Wal, Jeff said, 'long as they had three good arms between 'em he guessed they'd make out.

Whistle
on the River

BY GIFF CHESHIRE

Unlike the placid, muddy breadth of the Missouri, the second great river of the West did not readily lend itself to use as a waterway. Carrying a tremendous volume of water in a deeply scoured, rock-ribbed channel, the Columbia poses enormous navigational problems even today. From the dangerous Pacific Bar below Astoria to the confluence of the Snake, it is yet the nation's most powerful and hostile stream. But in the beginning it presented an even greater challenge, for it was apparent to all who first traveled its length that it provided the only practicable passage through successive ranges of mountains impenetrable to all except those who traveled on horseback or afoot. The battle to master practical navigation of the Columbia called forth a whole new breed of men who learned every bar, cataract, and idiosyncrasy of that violent river and built their knowledge into a whole new concept of river boats and river travel which persists to this day.
—T.W.B.

TITUS hated the shadows. Winter or summer the deep purple patterns tilted from the rearing, green-stippled mountains and fell across the silvered width of the river. The Landing and all the broad flat behind it were darkened, subdued, with the yellow splash of the sun never reaching them. Frisking down the Columbia gorge, a continual east wind knifed cold into creature and object; it built great glistening ice sheets on the rocky eminences to Washington and Oregon and turned the earth of the cove into a brittle plain over which the wooden wagons rattled and clattered.

The only open expanse was directly above, escaloped patterns of sky where light burned or glowed or snuffed to near-extinction; but a man could not walk always with uptilted head. Not even a man like Titus Evart, whom The Landing counted as its own.

Styles Evart was coming out of the machine shop, frowning, his slight figure bent as though billowed by the strong wind. Titus grinned to himself, thinking, "It's the same old story. He bristles like a bantam rooster, but the work doesn't get done. The *Jenny*'s still on the ways—and a long way from built."

His older brother was coming toward him. Styles Evart favored his mother's side of the line: the rather slight stature, the instinctive haughtiness, the deep-going sense of superiority that was forever translating itself into works and defeating its own aims. A grim amusement rose in Titus as he watched the nervous, short-stepped gait. This morning Styles had something special worrying him.

Styles grunted, "Come up to the office, Ty," and never stopped.

Titus turned from the ways on which the *Jenny*'s unfinished hulk lifted, the scent of oakum and calking cotton and heated tar tingling in his nostrils, the vibrant ringing from the machine shop beating his ears. The *Oriole,* which a little earlier had left mail and passengers at The Landing, sent a hoarse, muted whistle from some place on up the twisting gut of the gorge.

The small structure that was the office of the boatyard and wooden landing stood in the middle of an open area, a frozen gravel road running around it, along which sundry utility structures were strung. Styles shoved open the door. Inside, he removed his sheepskin greatcoat and knitted cap. In the doorway to the side room that was his private office he hesitated, turning back toward Titus with a stiff grin.

"The *Oriole* brought another letter from Curtis. He'll be up on the *Boniface* tomorrow. You know what that means."

"Yes. He's canceling the contract." Titus digested the news, not surprised at what had long been foreseen, but still a little shocked by its advent. "Well, you can see his point," he reflected. "We were to deliver the *Jenny* in October. Now it's November." The impulse was strong in him to add, "It's been the same with the last half-dozen boats." He resisted this, a delayed sympathy for Styles running through him. It wasn't Styles's fault; a man couldn't help the way he was born. If fault there was, it was Jonathan Evart's for dying, for getting himself killed by the very thing he had devoted much of his life to creating.

"What can we do about it, Ty?"

It wasn't often that Styles asked for advice, and now Titus grinned at him. "Let him warp his hull down to Portland. Tell him to take it and be damned! After all, there's the family pride!"

Anger crawled slowly across Styles's thin, arch-nosed face. "You're glad to see it, aren't you?"

"Not exactly. But it's no surprise."

"You could've managed things better?"

"I've never said that!" Instantly Titus regretted the savageness he let creep into his voice. His own deep dissatisfaction had tricked him into taking a foul swipe at Styles. When Jonathan had been crushed by a toppling hull, six years before, Titus had still been in school in Portland. Styles had not asked to have the heavy responsibility of The Landing thrust upon his young shoulders. But he had done his unselfish if inadequate best to meet the obligation. Titus said quickly, "I'm sorry, Styles. I don't know what gets into me."

Styles gave him a long look and turned away, and Titus knew the mood. He would talk no more on the subject—this proud twenty-six-year-old Styles Evart, with everything he had tried to do a failure around him—not with a brother four years his junior. Titus stood there a moment, trying to bring the right words to his tongue.

Through the front windows he could see the boatyard with its three ways, all but one empty and fallen into disrepair. Above ran the timbered tramway with its giant blocks and massive lines. The big steam donkey, intended for pulling steamboats onto the ways for repair, was there on skids, but it had been long since fire had warmed its boiler. Beyond was the dwindling pile of lumber, once the stockpile for repair work and new construction and now sparse and picked over because there was not money enough to keep it replenished. It was all stark evidence of dwindling prosperity, of approaching bankruptcy.

Against all this, Styles Evart had done his level best, and it had been insufficient. Yet Titus could not articulate these things. They were the intangibles that tied his own hands like new hemp rope. They were the things he hated yet could not voice to Styles without showing that hatred more than he cared to.

He went outside. The racket in the machine shop drummed up again, the east wind whipped tiny knives into his cheeks.

The dead could not return, yet it seemed that his father was always here. Lesser men could not pace to the tracks he had left about The Landing, and this was not their fault. Jonathan Evart had been a giant, a huge man with a rolling chuckle, who had only to conceive an idea to see its incarnation.

Some sense of the titan within him must have guided Jonathan Evart when he chose this site on the river, twenty miles above the town of Vancouver at the confluence of the Columbia and the Willamette, a thirty-acre flat at the base of deep mountains rising on the Oregon shore. When Titus was still a baby, Jonathan had started his woodyard, supplying fuel to the steamboats plying the river and connecting the fresh-water, inland seaport of Portland with the mineral-rich, emerging empire east of the Cascade Mountains. He had prospered, and he had added ways for the construction and repair of the packets and prospered more.

He had built a community that now crowded the flat, for his enterprises took the hands of many men, some to cut cordwood on the mountain, others, in summer, to haul it down to the yard and bank it out in unending ricks where the chipmunks barked. Still others were needed to load it onto the steamers, and many more to man the boatyard. Cut off from the world save for the passing steamers, this village of more than a hundred souls had been Jonathan's pride and joy, and over it he had reigned benign and supreme.

Titus passed now through the woodyard, an excitement that had been stirring in him since morning, and underlying all the rest, directing his steps toward the landing, where the packets stopped to discharge and pick up passengers, mail and small freight, besides taking on fuel. The *Bluebell* would start downstream presently, and though he knew that Ewen Barcliff would be on it, he wanted to witness the departure with his own eyes.

The wooden landing joined the village on the east. The *Bluebell,* downbound, had stopped there for wood, and Titus observed that he had guessed its leaving time closely. He saw Ewen Barcliff standing at the rail, but his gaze flicked quickly away from the man, turning to the slight figure it sought on the wharf.

Huldah Dalquist waved to Barcliff, who was her father, turned quickly and started for the far end of the dock, and Titus knew she had not noticed him. He hurried after her, overtaking her on the long slant leading down to the road connecting with the main street of the village.

Titus grinned and said, "I thought maybe you'd go with Ewen."

She looked at him quickly. "Why, no. I had nothing to go down about."

A pulse was crashing in Titus's ears, partly of fear and partly of expectancy. What if she suspected that he had plotted to send her father away overnight? Plotted to break the fence Ewen Barcliff had unintentionally built about his daughter simply with his presence? Plotted to give them a chance, at last, to see each other and clarify the thing between them?

He said, "Then you're not afraid to be alone?"

Huldah laughed. "Here at The Landing? A place even the sunlight can't reach?"

"You hate it, too, don't you?"

"Why—do you?"

"Yes."

After a long moment she said, "That's funny from a man who's being married tomorrow. You intend to live here, don't you?"

"Yes. I can't get away."

"Why are you telling it to me, Titus? Does Leonora know how you feel?"

"I don't suppose so. We've never talked about it." He looked at her askance, seeing her so tall and slender, so charged with something he could not understand, yet so gravely calm. He had to see her. He had to know what was there before to-morrow.

"You should have told her." They had come onto the main street of the village. Huldah stopped in front of the store and post office. "I've a few things to buy. If I don't see you again before the wedding, I wish you happiness, Titus. Leonora's a prize for any man."

He wheeled toward her, looking down into her deep brown eyes. "It's a long time until tomorrow."

Gravely, studiously, she regarded him, then turned quickly away and went into the store.

A guilty feeling came over Titus as he took a devious course back to the boatyard. It hadn't been quite what he expected when he had maneuvered to get Ewen Barcliff, who was the machine-shop foreman, sent to Portland to see about the cast-ings for the *Jenny*'s wheel journals. Yet he was certain that the deep chord forever struck in him by Huldah's presence, by the very thought of her, had its counterpart in her. Before tomorrow he had to know what it meant.

Striding along the frozen road, the decaying village all around him, Titus smiled without amusement. The Evarts owned every foot of ground and every structure on this small, flat chip at the base of the mountain, and the drain of it was what was ruining them. Despite their bluff and pretense, everybody knew that. Unable to admit the difficulties in which it had caught itself, the family could not retrench by slashing the big payroll, by lopping off this expense and that. Styles had a genius for losing business rather than attracting it. The Landing must rock on, proudly and stubbornly as it always had, until its final ruin. And Styles would brook no interference with his management.

Ruin was not far away now, and ruin would mean freedom, Titus reminded himself. Freedom from the purple shadows that so strangely could swell his heart with fear. Insistent in him again was the knowledge that he could save the yard if he could have the chance, if he could bring himself to rebel against Styles and Lambda Evart, his mother. For he was of Jonathan's flesh and blood and kind. He could make things move. He could start things humming again with daring, vision, and profit.

But even if he had the heart to take control away from Styles, would he want to save the yard? Its failure would mean that he could escape. Then, in time, he himself could pull the cord that ripped the hoarse scream of a packet through the deep chasms of the gorge, rather than merely hear it with deep, sick longing. Then there would be no question of gratitude to Styles, of family loyalty and pride, of a dead man's rights.

He had not wanted to return to The Landing after his two years of advanced schooling in Portland. Even in his boyhood its shadows had frightened him, giving him a gnawing hunger for light. He had planned, after school was finished, to defy Jonathan and go on the river. Then Jonathan had died, putting them all in the trap.

His boot heels thumping on the hard earth, Titus considered the unbreakable intangibles that bound him here. First there was Styles's deep need of his help in the task Styles had not elected for himself, even if Styles would not let him have any of the management. Behind that was the iron will of Lambda, to whom there was no alternative but the carrying out of Jonathan's will. Mortising it all was Leonora, beautiful and fragile and remote, whom he loved. Daughter of Luther Rockey, the yard superintendent and one of Jonathan's first employees, she, in turn, loved The Landing where she had been born. She would not consider leaving it, or having him away from her and off on the river.

In spite of Huldah Dalquist, tomorrow's marriage was urgent: Titus wanted it as quickly as possible. Leonora would save him, give him peace in his trap. He had to find this, for his savage urge, his bitter amusement at the plight of The Landing could not be entertained by an honorable man. He knew that, however much he might desire it, he could not make his way to the light in that fashion. The Landing could be saved and he would have to do it. Duty and Leonora would give him contentment in it if only he could find escape from the haunting image of Huldah Dalquist. Huldah was the keystone to the entire problem, and he thought he knew how to destroy her. Then tomorrow he and Leonora could be married. The day after tomorrow he could be happy here.

The whole trouble at The Landing was mismanagement; in a dozen ways he saw how this was true. Styles lacked Jonathan's driving force and easy dominance over others. There was a faint arrogance in him that aroused resentment, a bewildered but stiff-necked stubbornness.

If only Styles would not try to hide his helplessness behind bland persistence. The sly little that Titus, in his capacity of glorified clerk, could do toward achieving discipline and order, efficiency and economy, morale and good will, Styles countermanded imperiously with some move of his own. Styles could not accept his failure, and would not, and Lambda stood solidly behind him in everything. And always circumstances had prevented Titus from simply rebelling and clearing out. So, having to stay, he had to make it as painless as possible. He thought he knew the way.

The flames crackling in the big fireplace brought cheer into the large Evart sitting room. For days the larger, more pretentious parlor had been given over to the wedding. Now the rehearsal was over, with the bridesmaids, the best man, the stripling attendants gone. Lambda Evart and Leonora were still in there, engrossed in the small touches so unnoticeable to a man and so important to a woman. Styles was strumming on the big grand piano in the music room, with the Reverend Thomas, up from Portland to perform the ceremony, in a deep chair beside him, listening.

Titus was sprawled before the fire, alone in the sitting room, thinking of Leonora, of how bright-eyed and excited she had been, how beautiful and precious. When he had watched her, earlier, a pride of possession had come to him, and it lingered yet. He had always known her, and he had always loved her, but he was rushing her into this marriage, seeking stability for himself.

It was on this rising note of relish, his gaze deep in the cherry embers of the fire, that the fear struck him again, that nameless, baseless sense of apprehension that came so frequently of late. It started sweat in his pores and it shortened his breath and put a panic desire for movement in him. It came always when he was watching fire, seeing the red-hot tongues wrap about the fuel, consuming it. Now his hands tensed on the arms of his chair, and he sat upright, willing the fear away.

Styles's music splattered in his ears, and for a long moment he listened to it minutely, squeezing all else from his thought. Relaxation came slowly, letting his tall body bend back against the contours of the chair.

"After tomorrow!" he thought. "After tomorrow!" His desire for peace became a tremendous thing, his desire to surrender and receive the quieting stroke. A man could stand only so much of bitterness.

Styles was in his music, escaped into it, and for an interval, as he thought of it, a sense of deep sympathy came to Titus. In that moment he saw Styles objectively for the first time, the shy, slight male replica of Lambda, alien unto Jonathan but obedient to the last breath. Whatever had been Styles's secret dreams, he had never asserted them. Like Titus, he had gone through the village school, then had gone out to Portland for two finishing years. Then he had returned to The Landing to understudy Jonathan. What had he put down? What had Lambda herself put down in the three decades she had lived here, with only an occasional trip outside, in a web a man now dead had woven so tightly about them all?

Abruptly Titus thought, "We've never gone at it right. Always we've sensed the rivalry in each other. Styles knows I criticize him in my mind, hold him responsible for the fix we're in. That makes him stubborn, makes him meddle and ruin everything I do to try and get the yard running right. Tonight— no, in the morning—I'll tell him. That we can talk things over and work together. That we can pull out. It'd please Lambda. And Leonora."

He thought with strange interest of the sympathy between Leonora and Styles. Always she defended him, quickly and fiercely. "It's not his fault he wasn't ready when he had to take the full responsibility for things, Titus! He kept you on in school, didn't he? He was only doing what your father did to him, when he made you come back to the yard! He knew it was what your father wanted. Sometimes your . . . your smug superiority infuriates me, Titus!"

The last of the fear was gone, and a peace of sorts came to him. The sonorous clock on the mantel told him it was after ten. Leonora would be wanting to go home soon, and he would walk her down the hill. He would tell her on the way how right everything was going to be. He had to make it right. What man could not change, he had to accept, and to remain sane he had to accept it without rancor.

The hoarse cry of a steamboat whistle came through the night. Titus rose quickly and crossed to the big bay window that overlooked the river. The Evart house was perched on a small ledge above the village, and now he could see the scattered lights. There was the merest trace of a moon, enough that he could make out the dark, hulking silhouettes of the yard and the looming mountains on the Washington side. Then the packet drifted across his range of vision, almost indistinguishable save for the pinpoints of light at its ports and windows.

Excitement crawled in him. Yonder was mystery, color, stimulation, and warmth, the strange, gay, moving life that the steamers knew. The boat had whistled for nothing more than a cheery salute to the sleeping landing, and acknowledgment of the works of Jonathan, and now it passed on behind a distant screen of willows.

Sighing, Titus turned toward the parlor, halting in the big archway to watch his mother and Leonora rearranging the bower of artificial flowers for the tenth time. Leonora had not noticed him, and in the unguarded moment her lips were parted, her face alight with eagerness, like a child's. Again warmth stole through him. Here, too, was beauty and mystery. His own. Then she saw him and turned, smiling.

"I was ready to call you, Titus. I'd better be getting home."

Her small hand in the bend of his arm, his long pace shortened to match hers, they went down the winding, frozen road. Yet Titus found that he could not explain how he meant to settle things between himself and Styles, how he meant to find peace. And only once did she speak.

"It's going to be beautiful, Titus!"

"Life?"

"Well, that, too. But the wedding, I mean."

He was conscious of disappointment, aware briefly of the essential evasiveness of her. He had never yet caught her and pinned her down to an exact man-and-woman understanding. The marriage meant the beautiful wedding and the lovely gifts and her coming to live in the big Evart house, with its two servants. But that, he told himself, was the childish charm of her. He wanted to keep her so, a fragile, lovely child, enchanted and filled by the passing moment.

He did not go in, but kissed her at the front stoop, shyly, aware of the mechanicalness with which she met the gesture. Then he cut off toward the boatyard and walked aimlessly past it before he picked a devious route toward the house of Ewen Barcliff.

Huldah answered his slow rap almost instantly, giving him the impression that she had been expecting him. Yet she looked at him closely, saying, "Titus! Why?"

Without waiting for an invitation he stepped quickly inside. They regarded each other for a studious moment; then, with a slight laugh, Titus said, "Didn't you guess I would come?"

"I was . . . afraid of it, yes. Titus, you mustn't."

He pushed past her and found a chair and seated himself elaborately. She wore a different frock from the one she had worn that afternoon, which meant that she must have fixed herself up a little. Excitement leaped in him. She had expected

him, and now was only shy. She took a chair across the room
from him, sat straight and tense in it.

"Your trick in sending Father down to see about those forg-
ings was pretty obvious," she said.

He laughed again, but he was no longer quite so sure of himself. From the start he had at once felt a deep understanding of
Huldah Dalquist and had been as deeply baffled by her. She and
her father had been at The Landing only since spring. Fleetingly
he remembered his first glimpse of her, in the early summer.
He had been fishing, down below the point, and, looking up
absently, he had seen her standing on a rock. Sheltered in young
brush sprouts, he knew that he had not been observed, and he
stood watching her, the eternal river breeze pressing her skirt
tightly against her slim legs, and a deep excitement had kindled
in him.

Then he saw that she held a red rose in her hand. She stood
for a moment looking out over the river; then, leaning forward,
she dropped the flower into the water and in deep absorption
watched it float away. As she turned away she saw him, but
before he could move or call she hurried up the bank and
from sight.

He put the story together by himself from what he heard
later. She had been married for a year to a young packet officer, Herb Dalquist, who had died when the *Idaho Falls* had
blown up, three years before, just above Vancouver. Herb Dalquist's body had never been found, with only the image of him
left within her, as the image of her had, in that moment, impressed itself indelibly in Titus Evart's thoughts. The rose had
been a message to Herb Dalquist, and what it had contained
made a gnawing curiosity in Titus's mind.

They had met on frequent occasions since, at church and local
parties. She had never mentioned the incident. Yet she had
been aware of him, intensely aware of him, as he had been of
her. Titus had sensed that, sensed the fire that was in her, too,
knowing that he could direct it toward himself if he chose. And
now he confessed to the many little ways in which he had tried
to do this.

He said, "You don't want me to go, Huldah."

"What I want and what I have to do are different things. I know why you came, Titus, and I'm not flattered. You came to cheapen me. You thought if you could turn me into trash you could forget. In your way, you came to kill me."

It staggered him, the directness with which she went to the very core of the impulse that had moved him. Stubbornly, brutally, he said, "But I've got to forget you."

Huldah's laugh was low. "How simple men make everything!"

"Simple? No. It's a hell of a way from being simple."

"Did it occur to you, even, what will happen if somebody saw you come here?"

"I was careful of that. Nobody saw me. And nobody will see me go."

She smiled bitterly. "Then I'm perfectly safe, of course. See! You're succeeding in what you set out to do. You've turned me into trash in spite of me. You've made your mind accept the fact that I'm a woman you can visit this way. A gay . . . widow!"

He crossed to her, lifted her to her feet, and drew her to him. She resisted for only a moment, then suddenly let him take her lips. Finally she said, "If I thought I could make you free, Titus, I would. But it wouldn't be this way. You've succeeded with your murder. So go while you are as free as you are."

Enervation came to him with something of a shock, and he admitted what he had known from the start—that she was sincere. Obliquely he thought of the rose and the river, and savagely he said, "You were right. I was trying to destroy you to free myself. I had to see what was between us, and I've done neither of us any good. I'm sorry." And turning, he plunged from the room.

The sting of guilt and defeat were pronounced as he strode back up the hill toward the Evart house, which was now dark save for a lone light in what would be the music room. Titus's lips twisted bitterly, his passing sympathy for his brother destroyed. He was caught, caught, caught, and a part of his fury turned against Huldah, who had refused him escape, who had refused to reveal her mystery and make him free.

Leonora. Fleshless, immature spirit whom tomorrow he would marry. The rose, red as fire. He found that he was trembling, the old fear crawling in him again. There was no escape, no door, no light. Only the purple shadows of the mountains, forever beating into his nerves.

Halfway up the hill he halted and turned, letting his gaze sweep over the benighted village to dwell on the boatyard and the woodyard next to it. Fire. That was the obsession that had been in him, fire secretly set in the dry bark that would leap and growl and grow until The Landing was destroyed. This was what he had feared—that he would do it. No one would know, and he would be free, beyond the grasp of family loyalty and responsibility. He shook his head as though the idea could thus be dislodged and hurled from him, and started on up the hill toward the house.

He was nearly up the stairs when Styles's crisp voice said, "Ty!" and, turning, he saw his brother standing in the big archway below. Titus hesitated, then went back down, following Styles across the darkened sitting room to the music wing, where a pendant lamp burned low. Styles gestured toward a chair, himself taking the piano bench.

"I've made up my mind, Ty. You can save the yard. That's something I've always known and hated. You have all the gifts of Jonathan, but I've deliberately kept you from demonstrating them. You'll never have to learn what it is to face a responsibility you want to meet, only to find yourself not up to it. You're lucky, kid, and it's all yours. I'm getting out."

Titus whirled, shock and unreasoning anger spurting through him. "Mine! You're not shoving it onto my shoulders, now that you're finally dead up against it! I want no more of The Landing! For all of me, it can rot!"

Styles smiled, fleetly and bitterly. "Angry talk, kid. You and I have always been caught in the trap of a dead man's works. I've played out my part. Now I'm at the end, and I'm free. Yours is beginning. Since you won't fail, you'll never be free.

And maybe I'm not so poorly off, after all. Your ability will bind you; my weakness lets me out of it."

"But what do you mean to do?"

"I don't know yet."

Rebellion was crowding Titus close to recklessness. "Look here! I've got something to say about this. I hate the place! I'm getting out, myself!"

"Leonora would never let you. She was born here, and she loves it."

"Leonora'll do what I say!"

For the first time anger clouded Styles's eyes. "You're not making her unhappy, Ty. That I won't stand."

In sudden suspicion Titus rasped, "Are you in love with her?"

"I don't know. It was always you and she. Schoolmates, and then sweethearts. I've never even answered my own question about that. And now we'd better go to bed, kid. There's a wedding tomorrow, you know. Yours."

"Damn it, Styles, this is your mess. I tell you I'm clearing out."

"No."

The voice was Lambda Evart's, coming through the doorway. She entered the room in a faded silk wrapper, her faded eyes stern in the lamplight, her faded hair pillow-tossed. "I listened. I'll have no more of this talk, Titus."

Titus faced her. "I've reached the point where I don't give a damn about family pride. I don't give a damn if my father's work lives or dies. I don't give a damn about Styles's feelings. What right has a dead man to force me into something I hate?"

Lambda Evart took a seat, and in the lamplight her face looked strained and very old. "Because you are of his name and his blood. His responsibility becomes yours."

"Why?" Titus demanded. "Jonathan made his choice. He did what he wanted to do. What right did he have to plan the same thing for me? And Styles?"

"Because when a man creates something he is responsible for it. The village was founded on your father's idea. After that it became objective and no longer belonged to him alone. The village is people, people other than ourselves. There's a certain amount of coming and going, but most of them have been here for many years. They've planned their lives around The Landing. Some of the younger ones, like Leonora, were born here. Unless we Evarts keep it going, their lives will be seriously disrupted. We put life here and we have to sustain it. That is the relation between a man and his works. They've believed in us, and they've built on that belief. That's why Jonathan planned to have his work cared for after he was gone. That's why I've held his sons to it, cruel as it has seemed at times. I'll have no more of this talk. Do you understand, Styles?"

"Yes, Mother. I guess I always have."

"And you, Titus?"

"Yes, Mother." The tone was without conviction.

She turned in the doorway. "Good night," she said and was gone.

The red rose, red as fire. Titus waited until Styles had gone up to bed, and when he left the music room he turned, not toward the stairs, but toward the front door. Standing on the veranda, he heard the distant, re-echoing hail of a river boat. Resolution abruptly filled him.

What Lambda Evart had said was only the articulation of the things that had held him here, things he had felt without voicing, without clearly understanding. But things forged of the hardest steel. And yet what Lambda had said did not lessen the injustice. Jonathan should have known that one generation had no rights over the next.

The icy road beat solidly under his feet. Titus thought, "Styles himself claimed Jonathan is in me. And what Jonathan made, Jonathan could destroy. There can be no question of honor and duty to something that doesn't exist."

All around him lay the sleeping village. Titus made his way carefully down a back road, skulked along a rick-skirted lane of the woodyard. He had the exact spot in mind, the little shack the wood-handlers used when they came in out of the weather to get warm. The fire was kept banked with coal.

The shack was not locked, and he stepped into the dark warmth, his gaze going instantly to the low glowing red of the draft. He knew without seeing that there was kindling in the big coal bin in the corner. Shavings. A neat little wigwam of sticks. A match.

He was quite calm. He made the preparations, dragged a match alive, thrust it quickly against the kindling so that the light of it would not glow too long in the windows. He stepped outside, pulling the door shut gently. His mind was bright with a sort of detached interest. This was the ideal spot. Wood was piled closely around the shack, most of it cut since early summer, dry and tinder-barked, and there was trash. It was near the ways with their heavy spillings of grease and pitch and resin. The wind was right, the fire equipment scattered, the water lines frozen. He had only to be in bed before the fire was discovered.

He skulked up the hill, went silently into the house. From his room he could see a faint pink glow in the yard. He stared in exultation. The works of Jonathan were finished. The dead man's trap was destroyed!

A whistle sounded on the river.

It was only the screaming of a steamboat, somewhere in the twistings of the great gorge, echoing and re-echoing through the dark, looming mountains.

"No! No! No—no!"

The elation went out of him like a bursting bubble, and in its place was sudden terror. He bounded from the room and raced down the stairs and into the outer darkness. He stumbled through the woodyard with his lungs bursting in his chest.

He was too late. Flames had burst through the roof of the little shack. Now the lack of means of fighting them was a horror to him. Cupping hands to his lips, he screamed, "Fire! Fire!"

It quickly grew incoherent. The village was long trained in sleeping with one ear set for the sound of whistles in the night, for the particular signal that meant a packet was putting in for

wood. All Titus knew was that by the time he had found a
pail, filled it with river water at the foot of the ways, and
raced back up the long slope, other figures were hurtling through
the light from the dancing flames that now completely enveloped the wood-handlers' shack and were eating into the trash
pile behind, toward the woodricks. Running, shouting figures.
Titus now had only a numb emptiness where his mind had
been. A bucket brigade was formed. Fire leaped over two woodricks, now, and they were logs burning in a giant fireplace.

"The whole landing'll go, sure as you're a foot high!" somebody gulped. "The wind's set for it!"

"And the very day young Titus was going to get married!
What a shame!"

Then the figure of Styles loomed before him. "Get some men,
Ty! We've got to move the wood away from the fire! That way,
we can hem it in!"

The calmness in Styles's voice soothed him. Titus whirled,
bellowing, "Onto the woodpiles west of the fire! We've got to
clear a ring around it!"

He was obeyed with energy. On all sides of the spreading
flames the woodricks began to dwindle, as men, women, and
children picked up stick after stick and raced away. A half-
dozen men with wet gunny sacks stood solidly between the fire
and the boat ways. Abruptly Titus realized that a conflagration
had been prevented. Weakness hit him, his legs trembled, and
he thought he would fall.

These people, half clad and disdaining the freezing wind, were
fighting for The Landing. Here was what Lambda Evart had
meant. "Styles," he thought. "I've got to tell him that I set it."

He moved around the burning area hunting Styles. For the
first time he saw Leonora. She was on her knees in the road,
with others standing near, and something was stretched on the
frozen earth. Titus swerved forward and looked down.

"Styles, Styles," Leonora was saying over and over again.
"Styles."

"He's all right," a man told Titus. "He was working on the

leeward side in all that heat and smoke. He wouldn't come out till we carried him."

Titus turned away quickly.

It was midmorning when Titus, with a wrapped package under his arm, headed across the flat toward the river. There, squatting on the bank, he unwrapped the package.

It was a miniature steamboat. Titus squinted at it, hefting it, moving it from side to side. Then he placed it on the water. A little push, and it nosed out into the current. He watched it grow small in the distance, disappear at last in the hollows of the rippling surface. He straightened, turning, and saw the girl standing on the bank above him.

Huldah Dalquist came slowly down to him. "I saw you coming this way, Titus. I . . . I've worried about you. I followed you."

"I'm glad you did."

"What was it, Titus?"

"A model I made when I was a kid. I used to pretend I was its skipper. It's launched, at last. It's on the river."

"Are you sorry?"

"No. Glad."

"Then I want to tell you about the other time, when you saw me here. It was more than a sentimental gesture, Titus. It was farewell to things that couldn't be. It was facing the future. That's all a person can do."

Titus looked at her. "You heard the wedding's off, or you wouldn't have come here."

"Yes."

"Leonora told me, this morning. She didn't realize it was Styles until last night."

"They're suited to each other."

"And Huldah—I torched the woodyard, last night. I tried to destroy it."

"You never will, again."

"No. And now I want to forget it. And, Huldah—"

"Yes?"

"I'm glad I couldn't murder you. I'm glad you're whole—and here."

She laughed. "It's cold. Let's go."

The *Boniface* came in at noon. It brought Jared Curtis, manager of the big Cascade Line, for whom the *Jenny* was building. That he had come in anger was apparent the moment he stepped into the office. Coolly, Styles beat Curtis to the jump.

"You've come to cancel the contract, and I wouldn't blame you. I admit that things were pretty bad, but we've reorganized. I was only acting as a sort of regent, Curtis, until my brother was ready to take control. He did so, this morning, and he's already made some changes. Maybe you noticed there is activity around here."

"I did." Curtis's eyes appraised Titus. "Always said the boy's the spitting image of Jonathan. You know, your father built the Cascade Line its first boat, did our repair work. That's why we worried along with you. I came to tell you the deal's off. But now—how soon can you have her finished?"

"A week," Titus said. "But don't credit me with being Jonathan. I guess he split himself between the two of us. Styles and I are running The Landing together."

Curtis got up. "Well, split or whole, the river needs men like Jonathan was. Always has. Put The Landing on its feet again, and there'll be business."

Through the window Styles watched the portly figure moving down toward the ways. "That was easy," he breathed. "A whale of a lot easier than I ever thought it would be."

Titus smiled. "Not so easy, I guess. Jonathan put a lifetime into getting that kind of an answer out of Curtis." His gaze strayed beyond to the Washington side and the tips of the mountains, glowing in the cold winter sun.

Riverboat Fighter

BY BRIAN GARFIELD

The Colorado River today, from Grand Canyon to the Gulf of California, is a series of dammed-up lakes and dry beds where not even a toothpick will float. It is not widely known that for fifty years a thriving steamboat business operated there. This story is fiction, but its facts about the Mohave, *the steamboat company, and Jack Mellon are true.*
— T.W.B.

CLAY Goddard came aboard the *Mohave* at Yuma an hour before she was due to depart. He walked around "B" Deck to his regular tiny stateroom on the portside and remained there only long enough to stow his carpetbag and comb his hair; the cubicle was stifling hot. Coming out on deck, he tugged his brocade vest down and placed his gray hat squarely across his brows. Clay Goddard was a tall man, thin to the point of gauntness, with the hint of a stoop in his broad shoulders. His lion-gray eyes were hooded and his lips were guarded by the full sweep of a tawny mustache.

He was coming around the afterdeck, passing in front of the wide paddlewheel, when his alert eyes shot toward the gangplank. A solid-square man in a dusty blue suit was coming up the plank; sight of that man arrested Clay Goddard: he stood bolt still, watching, while the stocky man ascended to the rail and paused.

A ball-pointed brass star glittered on the newcomer's blue lapel. The ship's captain, coming toward the gangway, nodded and touched the brim of his cap. "How do today, Marshal?"

Marshal Emmett Reese nodded and said something Goddard didn't catch; then the lawman's deliberate voice lifted: "Believe I'll be going up with you this trip, Jack. How's the current running?"

"Slow and easy," Captain Jack Mellon said. He was a legend

on the river: he had steamed the Rio Colorado more than fifteen years. It was said he could talk to the river and hear its reply. He said to the marshal, "Ought to make an easy five miles an hour going up. I figure to make Aubrey's Landing in forty-eight hours."

"That's traveling," Marshal Reese observed. Clay Goddard watched the lawman's profile from his stance under the shadowed overhang of the afterdeck. The captain spoke once more and turned to go up the ladder toward his wheelhouse on the Texas Deck, and Marshal Emmett Reese's glance came around idly. His eyes alighted on Clay Goddard and immediately narrowed; the marshal's whole frame stiffened. Goddard's expression remained bleak, unreadable. Across thirty feet of deck space their glances clashed and held. The revolver butt at Goddard's hip touched the vein of his thin wrist.

Emmett Reese seemed about to advance, about to speak; but then the sound of an approaching buggy clattered toward the wharf, and the marshal ripped his eyes away, swinging heavily around, tramping back down the plank.

Clay Goddard's face revealed no particular relief. He turned with deliberate paces and walked into the ship's saloon. The bartender was its only occupant. Goddard took a cup of coffee, went to a table in the back of the room, and laid out an elaborate game of patience. Brooding over the cards, he sipped the cooling black coffee and ran his glance once around the room.

It was neither so large nor so elegant as the cardrooms on the great Mississippi packets; but then, this was Arizona, and rivers did not run so deep or wide here. It was engineering marvel enough that the *Mohave,* one hundred fifty feet long and thirty-three feet abeam, could carry two hundred passengers and a hundred thousand pounds of cargo and still skim over the Rio Colorado's shallow bottom. The water often ran less than three feet deep; the *Mohave* drew only thirty inches, fully ballasted.

Steamboats had been plying the river for twenty-seven years now, but their interloping presence in the desert country never failed to strike Goddard as an odd phenomenon. The ships of

the Colorado Steam Navigation Company regularly made the
seemingly impossible run up to Callville, Nevada—six hundred
miles above the river's mouth, and desert country all the way,
except where the big ships had to winch themselves up over
cascades through the knife-cut tall gorges upriver.

The saloon was a plain oblong room, low ceilinged and plainly
furnished—not at all like the velvet-lined rooms of the New
Orleans sternwheelers. But the *Mohave* was pride of the line,
and in the far Southwest she was queen. The barkeep wiped
his plain mahogany counter and behind it, between racks of
labeled bottles, hung a lithographed calendar with today's sailing date circled: *August 24, 1879.* Regarding that, and recalling
the grim square-hewn face of Marshal Emmett Reese on deck,
Clay Goddard thought what a long time it had been, how the
years had flowed silently by; and he felt quietly surprised. He
was thirty-seven this month; his birthday had passed, he suddenly realized, without notice.

His lean hands darted over the wooden table, placing card
upon card. Green sleeve garters held the shirt back from his
wrists. He pulled out his snap-lid pocket watch—eight-thirty in
the morning, and already he was soaked with sweat. It would
hit a hundred and ten inside the saloon today.

His gambler's training laid a cool endurance over him; over
the years he had developed the ability to stand off from himself and look on, as if from some long distance. Without it, his
life would not have been bearable.

The boat swayed gently as heavy freight wagons rolled up the
plank onto the cargo decking. Faintly through the door came
the hoarse shouts of teamsters, the profane calling of stevedores.
Passengers, early arriving, began to drift in and out of the saloon.
With a hissing chug and a resigned clatter, the boilers fired up
and began to build up their head of steam. Smoke rose from the
twin tall stacks at the front of the pilothouse.

His shirt drenched, Clay Goddard unbuttoned his elaborate
vest—the uniformed sign of his calling—and bent over his soli-
taire board in concentration. He was like that, frowning over
the merciless cards, when a great force rammed the edge of

the table into his belly, slamming him in his chair back against the wall.

Tautly grinning, a hawk-faced man stood hunched toward Goddard, a tall, powerful man with a stiff brush of straight red hair standing up brightly on his head. Hatless, the grinning man held the table jammed against Goddard, pinning Goddard to his chair. In a quiet, soft tone, the red-haired man said, "Somebody told me you were working this boat."

Goddard said with deceptive mildness, "Take the table out of my gut, Miles."

Miles Williams took his hands away from the table and laughed unpleasantly. "I ain't got my gun on just now. That's a piece of luck for you, Clay."

"Or for you."

Miles Williams' eyes met Goddard's without guile. "Nobody said you weren't tough, Clay, and nobody said you weren't fast. But I can take you."

"You can try," Goddard answered evenly. He pushed the table away from him and straightened his rumpled vest, but he kept his seat. The cards had flown into disarray when Williams had violently rammed the table. Goddard gathered them unhurriedly into a pack, never releasing Williams from his gaze.

Williams said, "I've got a lot to settle with you for, Clay. Too much to let pass. I'm going up to Aubrey on this boat and I don't figure both of us will get there alive."

"That's up to you, Miles."

"We're still in port. You can get off now. Maybe I won't follow you—I got business upriver."

Goddard tilted his head slightly to one side. "You'd offer me a chance to skin out, would you? I'm surprised."

"I ain't an unfair man," said Miles Williams. "And I don't like killing. Go on, Clay—get off the boat. Save us both a lot of grief that way."

Goddard considered him over a stretching interval of time; at the end of it he shook his head. "I guess not, Miles."

"Suit yourself." Abruptly, with a snap of his big shoulders, Miles Williams swung away and stalked out of the saloon.

At the bar, a few men with cigars and coffee had watched with careful interest. What Goddard and Williams had said had been pitched too low to reach their ears, but the scene had been too charged with action and hard stares to escape their attention. Sweeping them with his guarded eyes, Goddard maintained his cool expression and proceeded to lay out a fresh, slow game on the table.

Shortly thereafter, however, he got up and walked slowly out of the saloon. A deck hand was coiling in the stern rope. The ship was crowded with Army men—two companies of infantry on their way to Ehrenberg, shipping point for the inland Apache-fighting garrisons. Goddard threaded his path among the knots of troopers and entered his little stateroom, where he closed the door in spite of the heat building up. Out of his carpetbag he took ramrod, patches, cloth, and oil. After locking the door he dismantled his revolver and gave it a careful, methodical cleaning. Then he put it back together, loaded the cylinder with six .44-40 cartridges, and let the hammer down gently between the rims of two shells. Standing up, he slid the weapon into its oiled holster and adjusted the hang carefully. His expression never changed; the mustache drooped over his wide lips. He packed the cleaning equipment away, unlocked the door, and stepped out on deck just as the captain shouted from two decks above and the boat slowly churned out into the current.

The wharves and shipyard of Yuma slowly drifted past the starboard beam; there was a last glimpse of Fort Yuma, high on the hill with its precious squares of green lawns, and then the massive rolling paddlewheel drove the ship around the outer curve of the first bend, and the only sight to either side was mosquito-buzzing brushy lowlands and, beyond, the flats and dry-rock hills of the vast Southwestern desert.

Goddard stepped past a lashed-down freight wagon, and halted abruptly.

Coming forward, arms linked, were Marshal Emmett Reese

and a slim figure of a woman. Holding the woman's left hand was a girl of six, wide-eyed and with hair the same tawny color as Goddard's own. The woman's mouth opened and, quickly, Emmett Reese stepped out in front of her as though to protect her. Reese said nothing but it was plain by his stance and attitude that he expected Goddard to go on about his business without stopping to speak.

The woman put her hand on Reese's arm. "No, Emmett. We'll be on this boat for two days and nights. It's a small boat. We can't pretend to each other that we don't exist."

Goddard stepped forward with the briefest of cool smiles. "It's been a long time, Margaret." His glance dropped to lie on the little girl. "Six years," he murmured.

The woman had both hands on the little girl's shoulders now. Emmett Reese said, "Come on, Margaret, we can—"

"No," she said. "I want to talk to him, Emmett."

Reese's eyes bored into Goddard, but it was the woman his words addressed: "I wish you wouldn't."

"Take Cathy with you, will you? I'll meet you in the lounge." The woman's voice was firm.

Troubled, the marshal reached down to take the little girl's hand. He said to Goddard, "Miles Williams is on board."

"I know."

"This boat's in my jurisdiction. I don't want trouble."

"I won't be starting any trouble," Goddard said.

The little girl watched with her head tilted on one side, looking up at Goddard and then the marshal, puzzled but silent. Soldiers milled past in pairs and groups. An officer moved through the crowd, creating a stir of saluting and mumbled greetings. The woman, tossing her head impatiently, said, "Go on, Emmett." She bent down. "Go with the marshal, sweetheart. Mummy will be along soon."

The little girl stared at Goddard. "Who's he?" she demanded accusingly.

The woman looked up and away; her eyes turned moist. Emmett Reese said gently, "Come on, Cathy," and led the little girl away by the hand, casting one warning glance back toward Goddard.

Goddard moved toward the rail, pushing a path through for the woman. She came up and stood beside him, not looking at him, but watching the muddy flow of the river. Her eyes were still clouded with tears; there was a catch in her throat when she spoke: "I'm sorry. I knew this moment would come. I meant to be strong—I didn't mean it to be this way. But when she asked *who you were*—"

"She looks a little like me," he said musingly.

"She has your hair, your eyes—every time I look at her I—" The woman's head turned sharply down against her shoulder, hiding her face. Goddard's hand came out toward her, but stayed, and he did not touch her. A solemn mask descended over his face. He murmured, "Well, Meg."

He took a folded handkerchief from his vest and offered it to her. She pressed it to the corners of her eyes. She was a blue-eyed woman, slim and pretty but no longer in the smooth-cheeked paleness of youth: the veins of her hands and the creases around her eyes revealed that she was near Goddard's own age.

He said, "You're traveling with Emmett?"

"In separate staterooms," she said dryly, and then shook her head. "He wants to marry me—marry us, that is. He loves Cathy."

"Maybe," Goddard said softly, "that's because he's had the chance to love her."

Her eyes lifted dismally to his. Plainly gathering herself, she used both palms to smooth back her brown hair. "I am going to be strong, Clay," she said, measuring out each word for emphasis. "You and I, we had our chance together."

"And I ruined it," he finished for her.

"You," she agreed, "and that." She was looking at the worn-smooth handle of his revolver. "And now Miles Williams is here. He's been looking for you a long time, Emmett said. You killed two of his friends in a card game."

"I caught them cheating together. They drew against me."

"Is that an explanation, Clay?" she asked. "Or just an excuse?"

She reached out; her fingertips touched the walnut gun grip. "You love that thing."

"No. I hate it, Meg."

She swung half way, facing the river again, the marshes drifting past. The huge paddlewheel left a pale yellow wake stretching downstream with the current. "I wish I could believe you," she said. "If it's true then you've changed."

"I have," he agreed simply.

She threw her head back. Her voice was stronger: "We were married once. It didn't work. I've no reason to believe it would work again."

He nodded; but his eyes were sad—he was looking forward, toward the lounge where the little girl had gone. He said, "What will you tell her about me? She wants to know who I am."

"I don't know," she said, almost whispering. "I wish I did." She turned from him and walked away, moving briskly. He watched the way she walked, head turned over his shoulder, both hands gripping the rail so tightly his knuckles shone white.

A tall, red-topped figure swayed forward, pushing soldiers aside roughly with hands and elbows. Miles Williams reached Goddard's side and grinned around the cigar in his teeth. "Who's the lady, Clay?"

When Goddard made no reply, Williams said, "I saw you talking to Emmett Reese. With him on board, we're going to have a little problem, you and me. Either one of us starts trouble, he's likely to step in. So I've got a little proposition for you. I gave you your chance to get off the ship. You stayed, so I guess that means you want to play the game I called. All right, we'll lay down some ground rules. We wait, you and me. These soldier boys get off at Ehrenberg in the morning and the boat'll be less crowded tomorrow. Tomorrow night the decks ought to be pretty clear. We wait until everybody's asleep. No witnesses, that way. We have at each other, and no matter who's standing up afterward, ain't nobody can tell Emmett Reese who started the fight. The winner claims self-defense, and Reese can't dispute it, see? No law trouble, no trouble afterward for the one of us that's still alive."

"You're a coldblooded buck," Goddard observed without much emphasis.

"I just like to keep things neat," Miles Williams said, and turned aft. A holstered pistol slapped his thigh as he walked through the crowd.

Showing no sign of his feelings, Clay Goddard went into the saloon, picked a table, and set the pack of cards out, advertising his calling. It was not long before five soldiers were gathered round his table, playing low-stake poker.

The day passed that way for Goddard, bar sandwiches and coffee and poker—a steamy hot day that filled the room with the close stink of sweat weighted with tobacco smoke and the smells of stale beer and whisky. He did not leave the saloon until suppertime, when he went forward into the dining salon. He saw Emmett Reese and Margaret and little Cathy at the captain's table. His eyes lingered on the blonde little girl. Margaret's eyes found him once, but turned away quickly; she swung her head around, tossing her hair, to respond to some light remark of Captain Jack Mellon's.

Miles Williams was not in the room. Goddard took his customary place at the first officer's table, between the deck steward and an Army doctor, and ate a silent meal. Afterward he had a cigar on deck, and returned to the saloon for the evening's trade. The crowd was thoroughly penny ante; he made a total of seven dollars for the day's gambling, and went on deck at midnight. He had to pick a path over the heaps of sleeping soldiers.

The heat had dissipated with darkness. He lay down on his bunk, knowing he needed sleep in order to be alert for the following night's encounter; but sleep evaded him and he lay in the dark cabin with his hands laced under the back of his head, staring sightlessly at the ceiling. The engines throbbed soporifically, but he was still awake at three when the boat scraped bottom on a sand bar and the engines reversed to take her off. She lurched forward once again, going around the bar, and finally Goddard drifted into a semiwakeful drowsiness that descended into fitful sleep.

He was awake and dressed at dawn when the *Mohave* berthed at Ehrenberg. The town was a drab oasis at best. Miles Williams came by and said, "You could still get off right here and wait till the boat comes back down. But then maybe you'd rather not wait another three years for me to come after you again."

"Never mind," Goddard told him.

"All right," Williams drawled. The sun picked up glints in his bush of red hair. He grinned and ambled away. Goddard noticed Emmett Reese standing not far away, watching him inscrutably; it was hard to tell whether Reese had heard what had been said.

The soldiers disembarked with their baggage and wagons, and thus lightened, the boat made faster headway upstream. Its decks were lashed with wagonloads of mining machinery for the camps served by Audrey's Landing, but pedestrian traffic was light and there was hardly any trade in the saloon all day.

After supper he was on deck, savoring his cigar, when Margaret came out of the dining room and sought him out. If he was surprised, he did not show it. She said, in a voice that showed how tightly throttled were her emotions, "That may be your last cigar. Have you thought of that?"

"Yes."

"How can you keep such a rein on yourself, Clay? Aren't you frightened?"

He made no answer. He squinted against the cigar smoke and Margaret said, "You're scared to death, aren't you?"

"I guess I am."

"Then that's changed, too."

"Maybe I've learned to care," he said. He turned to look at her. "Sometimes it takes a long time to learn a simple thing like that."

His talk appeared to confuse her. She folded her arms under her breasts. "Cathy still wants to know about you."

"Have you decided what to tell her?"

"I'll tell her the truth. But I'm going to wait until tomorrow."

He said quietly, "You think I'll be dead by then, don't you, Meg?"

"One way or the other," she said. "Dead to us, anyway. Whether you're still walking and breathing won't matter." She dropped her arms to her sides; her shoulders fell. "Emmett told me that Miles Williams gave you the chance to get off at Ehrenberg."

"I might have taken it," he said, "except for you and Cathy. I wanted to have another day—this is as close as I've ever been to her. I couldn't give it up."

She said in a muted voice, "If you'd gotten off the boat," and did not finish; Goddard finished it for her:

"You'd have come with me?"

"I don't know. How can I say? Maybe—maybe."

Twilight ran red over the river. The great paddles slapped the water and a lone Indian stood on the western bank, silhouetted against the darkening red sky, watching the boat churn past into gathering night. A shadow filled the dining-room doorway, blocky and sturdy—Emmett Reese, who wore the star. Reese stood there, out of earshot, watching but not advancing. Goddard said, "I guess he loves you."

"Yes."

"And you him?"

She didn't answer right away. There was a sudden break in Goddard's expression and he seemed about to reach out and grasp her to him, but he made no motion of any kind and his face resumed its composure. He said slowly, "I have always been in love with you. But I have to meet Miles Williams tonight and my love for you can't stop that."

"Nor my love for you?" she cried out.

"I'm sorry," he said dismally.

Her voice subsided in resignation. "I can't give my little girl a father who fights to kill."

"What about Emmett Reese?" He was looking at Reese, outlined in the doorway, still as a mountain.

"It's his job. Not his pleasure." Her lip curled when she said it.

"It's no pleasure to me either," he said. "God knows there are a lot of things I regret, Meg."

"But you won't give up your pride."

"Would I be a man without it?"

She had no answer for him. She turned and walked from him, toward the waiting shadow of the marshal.

The cigar had gone dry and sour. Goddard tossed it overboard and went into the saloon. Lamplight sent rays through the smoky air; the crowd was thin and for an hour no one came to Goddard's table. He sat with the pack of cards before him; he sat still, his head dipped slightly like a tired man half asleep.

Miles Williams came at ten-thirty and sat down opposite him. Williams had a cheroot uptilted between his white teeth. His face was handsome and brash, the eyes half-lidded. "A friend is a close and valuable thing," he said. "I lost two friends one night."

"They forced it on me."

"Then they should have won." Williams picked up the deck of cards and shuffled it. "Blackjack suit you?"

And so they played a macabre game of cards while the hours ran out, while the passengers drifted away one by one and lamps winked out around the ship. The engines thrummed, the paddles hit the water with a steady slap-slap, and when the saloon was empty but for the bartender, Miles Williams said in a suddenly taut voice, "All ready, Clay?"

"Here?"

"On deck. Loser goes overboard. Neat—neat that way."

"All right," said Clay Goddard.

Williams thrust his chair back with his knees and stood. "After you?"

"Right beside you," Goddard answered, and they left shoulder to shoulder.

The decks were deserted; lamps were off, except two decks higher up on the Texas, where the keen-eyed captain swept the river vigilantly for shifting sand bars. Miles Williams said, "Jack Mellon's got eyes in the back of his head. We'll go on down to the afterdeck—he can't see that from up there."

They tramped along the port "B" deck and Goddard felt moisture on his palms; he wiped them on his vest and heard Williams chuckle. "Got you nervous, ain't I? Get a man nervous, you got the edge." Williams was flexing his fingers. Starlight glittered on the river. Not a single lamp glowed in the after section of the ship. The two men reached the platform behind the cabin structure. Here the smash of the paddles against the water was a loud racket in the night; the paddles lifted overhead and swept down, splashing drops of water against the stern and the aft yard or two of deck planking. The iron railing protected passengers from the cruel, deliberate power of the great paddlewheel.

Miles Williams stopped six feet from the rail and wheeled, planting his feet wide apart. "You can step back a way," he said calmly, "or do you want it point-blank?"

"Right here will do," Goddard said. "A man wouldn't want to miss his shot for bad light."

A startled brightness gleamed from Williams' eyes. "You steadied down quick, didn't you?" he observed. Then he laughed with raucous brashness. But the laugh fell away and his face grew long. The brush of his hair stood up against the sky and he suddenly cried, *"Now!"*

Williams' hand spilled for his gun butt. Close in to the man, Goddard did not reach for his own gun; instead he lashed out with his boot. The hard toe caught Williams' wrist just as the gun was rising. The gun fell away, bouncing off Goddard's instep; and Williams, rocked by the kick, windmilled back, off balance. His feet slipped on the wet planking; the small of his back rammed the stern rail and Goddard, rushing forward, was not in time to prevent Williams from spilling over backward into the descending paddlewheel.

The paddles caught Williams and dragged him down relentlessly; there was a brief awful cry, and that was all.

Gripping the rail, Goddard looked down into the churning blackness of the descending paddles. His eyes were hollow. Heavy footsteps hurried toward him along the deck and he turned, nerved up to high pitch.

Emmett Reese said, "I couldn't stop it before it started. But I saw it. He wasn't fast at all—you could have outdrawn him with no trouble."

"I knew that."

"You didn't figure on this?"

"No. I expected a good beating might have changed his mind." Goddard smiled bleakly. "I was always pretty good with my fists."

"Better than guns," Reese said quietly, staring at the heavy falling paddles. He added in a murmur that was barely audible over the slapping wheel, "You're a far better man than I gave you credit for, Clay."

Reese's hand reached out and clenched Goddard's arm. Goddard shook his head slowly back and forth, as if to clear it. He pulled away and walked forward along the empty deck.

He was in his cabin, unhooking his gun belt, when light knuckles rapped the door. When he opened it, Margaret stepped inside. The lamp washed her face in warm light.

She said, "Emmett told me what happened. You could have drawn on him. You could have shot him down, but you didn't —you tried to save his life."

"I told you," he said wearily. "A man learns a few things as time goes by, Meg."

She said, "Cathy's asleep now, and I didn't want to wake her. But in the morning when she asks me who you are, I'll be able to tell her. We'll have breakfast together, the three of us."

"What about Reese?" he said.

She moved into the circle of his arms. "He understands," she said. She turned her face up toward him.

Peaceful
John

BY KENNETH FOWLER

In the broad spectrum of Western settlement, a seldom-recognized but tremendously influential element were the immigrant men and women who also became emigrants in the great migration to the Pacific. In a very real sense, theirs was the most hazardous and challenging adventure, for they were already on foreign soil when they set foot on the Eastern Seaboard—or, at a later date, sailed into the mushrooming new metropolis within the Golden Gate. Chiefly of Northern European origin, they faced not only the now-familiar barriers of mountain and plain but also those of language, tradition. It is a permanent tribute to the courage of these people and their devotion to the personal freedom and opportunity they came to find that many north-country names are so familiar and often famous on the maps of the West and among its people. —T.W.B.

JOHN Remsberg reined up the dun in front of the ranch house's weed-fringed doorstep, halting the buckboard. The low-roofed weathered adobe stood commandingly on a ridge overlooking a coffee-colored creek which lost itself in sinuous wandering a half mile distant, in a motte of cottonwoods.

Hunched forward on the buckboard seat, Remsberg sat motionless for a long moment and with an air of introspection gazed out upon the biggest, the wildest, the loneliest stretch of country he had ever seen. The sand and rock and tough, spiny vegetation molded into rolling hills that ran as far as the eye could reach. The sky above them was an immaculate blue dome, anchored against remote peaks. The air of a fine September day fairly sparkled.

PEACEFUL JOHN by Kenneth Fowler originally appeared in *Zane Grey's Western Magazine*. Copyright 1953 by Kenneth A. Fowler.

Savoringly, Remsberg drew its tang into his lungs. The view from what was now his own dooryard made him feel little—and big. Little because of its immensity. Big because it strangely gave him a sense of liberation and power. Because this land was so virginal and big, it built bigness in a man's thoughts.

His right foot dangled over the edge of the buckboard. He swung it idly, enjoying the warmth of the sun soaking through his frayed cotton shirt and into his solidly thewed shoulders. He wore homespun breeches, and a campaign hat of the Union Army, stripped of its identifying insignia, lay cocked back on his broad head, exposing a swatch of straw-colored hair, flagrantly awry. His eyes, of a faded blue-denim hue, scanned the horizon with a fixed look of abstraction.

Ja. He nodded solemnly to himself, reflecting. *A land like this puts a fever in a man. It works into his blood and bones, like the feeling he can get from one special woman.* And suddenly he wondered. Was it the land stirring this peculiar restlessness in him, or the still vivid image of the girl he had met at Ellsworth's Mercantile this morning, when he had bought his supplies?

Of her he must not think. An aristocrat. He had heard of the Ellsworths, one of the oldest families in the region. Their house on the outskirts of town was the biggest in the neighborhood, and Abby Ellsworth had been raised as a lady of quality. Undoubtedly she worked in her father's prosperous business establishment only now and then, for something to do. And what was he? Ten years ago he had landed on the shores of this country, in New York, from the deck of a cattle boat.

Dream then, John Remsberg. But do not be a fool!

There had been a way about her, though—a frank and open manner almost blunt, yet inoffensive.

She had called him at once by his name, as if knowing all about him, and when he had shown surprise at this, her eyes, a soft and smoky gray, had twinkled. "This is the town's gossip forum, Mr. Remsberg," she had told him, smiling. "You are the man they call 'Peaceful John,' aren't you—the one who is taking over the old August Remsberg place?"

It was more a statement than a question and he merely nodded, seeming really to see her then for the first time—a slender, vital girl wearing a dress of some woolly dark green material and with black hair that shone like ice where it was plaited at the nape of her neck into a graceful chignon.

"Why do they call you 'Peaceful,' Mr. Remsberg?"

He looked down at her searchingly. "It is funny—that name?"

"Yes and no. It is, applied to you, I guess," and her eyes frankly measured his stalwart frame.

She made him think of an impudent puppy, teasing for attention. He said: "It is not funny in the north, not to carry a gun," and pondered solemnly. "Here it is a big joke, if a man does not?"

"It's unusual. Times are unsettled. Most ranchers wear them —for self-protection."

He held up his big fists before her. "These are my protection. I fought in the war for the Union. I have seen enough of guns. Now we are all neighbors again."

"Even neighbors quarrel, Mr. Remsberg. Down here you are less apt to meet trouble with a gun than without one."

"I mind my own business. I have no trouble." And he handed her the scrap of paper on which he had methodically written down the list of staples he required.

She apparently noticed his cautious pricing of each item as she laid it upon the counter, for when the order was completed, her mention of credit had an overdrawn casualness.

"Your uncle always ran an account here," she told him. "Pay us when you are able."

Color sprang in his cheeks as he spread the coins from a worn money pouch before her.

"I am able to pay for what I buy."

"Do you know what I suspect, Mr. Remsberg? I suspect that you are being foolishly proud! I could see only a few coins left in your purse."

Her outspokenness faintly shocked him. He stared at her and was surprised at the briefness of his discomfiture. Her words were blunt, but without sting. Popcorn cracked, but then you saw the golden kernel. And caught the savor. Her straight way of looking at him was not bold, but had simply an unaffected human curiosity—a kind of warmth. Then he noticed her hands, and had a sinking awareness of the gap between them. They were slim and unroughened, with fingers meant for delicately holding a wineglass or skimming gracefully over the keys of a piano. The hands of a lady.

Without visible effort he hoisted the heavy gunny sack of provisions and heaved it across his shoulder. Then he picked up the pouch.

"This pouch will not remain empty," he said stiffly.

"Of course it won't! You should do very well if you go after mavericks. I have heard of some fine herds being built up that way."

The warm animation in her voice made him instantly ashamed.

"Yes," he agreed, "I would like to build up a herd," and for an instant felt an awkward interrogation in their crossed glances.

"You must visit us again when you are in town."

"These stores will last me a long time."

"You will not want your nose at the grindstone all the time." She smiled. "Unless you intend to become a hermit."

Now, sitting hipshot on the buckboard's straw-cushioned seat, John Remsberg tried to shut her from his thoughts as he stared out over the ranch's run-down outbuildings. He had his supplies. Now he must get to work. There was brush to be cleared, sheds to be repaired, and somewhere out there in the brasada he must build a holding pen for the mavericks he hoped to rope and brand. A man could not let himself be distracted and still do the job he had to do here.

She had worn paper sleeve guards over the lacy cuffs of her blouse, so as not to soil them. And so tiny she had looked, standing beside him. Just one of his hands would have gone around her waist.

But the cattle. They must come first. Cattle that had multiplied extravagantly during the war years, and now could be legally claimed by the first man to go out and dab his loop on them.

Ach, but those dainty hands of hers! Wives of ranchers he had seen, waiting for their husbands in buckboards and spring wagons in town, had not had such hands.

Ja. The cattle first. And up north, in centers like Abilene, Ellsworth, Dodge City, were the buyers, ready and waiting, and already great dusty herds were thundering northward across the plains, and opportunity was for the foremost.

The hands of the ranchers' wives had been reddened and ugly —work hands. But was that all a man wanted of his woman— work?

Squinted against the brassy sunlight, John Remsberg's eyes built their dream as he stared out over the craggy, tawny hills. He shook his head, slowly, thoughtfully. No, he must not let himself be sidetracked. Besides, there was the talk about him in town—and what woman would want a man who disregarded the country's frontier code of law by the gun, and thus held himself up to scorn and ridicule?

Damnyankee carpetbagger! Won't last here six months. All those backhanded whisperings and slyly amused glances he encountered now, whenever he was seen in town.

Peaceful John . . .

He broke with a start from his introspection. Two riders had come up to the edge of the ranch yard and now sat saddle there, blowing their lathered horses as they talked briefly together, staring down at him. Then, suddenly, they swung their mounts into the yard, and reining in alongside the buckboard, dismounted.

One of the men was broad and stocky, with heavily jowled jaws and chilly eyes that lay on Remsberg with a studying fixity. His companion was small, almost runty. He sucked on the stub of a brown paper cigarette, his amber-toned eyes narrowed against a twirl of smoke.

The bigger man stepped up beside the buckboard. "Name of Dan Shiffley," he said, and stretched out his hand. With faint surprise, Remsberg met it. Shiffley nodded across his shoulder. "My partner, Maxie Fass."

Fass's head jerked slightly.

"I am pleased to meet neighbors," Remsberg said.

Shiffley grunted. "Heard in town you were takin' over here. Waste your time on a cocklebur outfit like this."

"Is so?" Remsberg asked mildly, but Shiffley ignored the remark.

"Come to offer you a job," he said. "Pay you fifty cents a head on every cow you can put in my Dollar S iron. Get the hang of it, you could do six a day, easy."

"Three dollars a day," Fass said. "Good pickin's for a greener."

Remsberg's mouth made a closed smile.

"Then I pick for myself—no?"

Shiffley looked at Fass. "Didn't I tell you, Maxie?" His glance swung to the sack of provisions canted against the back of the buckboard seat. "All set to lay in his store-boughts—see? Too almighty proud to hire out and turn a quick dollar."

Remsberg flushed. "I did not say it that way! I—"

"Only we got no hard feelin's, have we, Maxie?" Shiffley broke in. "Let's give Peaceful John here a hand with that sack."

Remsberg was not quick enough, leaping out of the buckboard. Shiffley was already at the back of the rig, tugging on the loaded gunny sack. As Remsberg lunged to seize it from him, the top fell open and its contents spewed out.

"Doggone!" Shiffley looked dumbly surprised as his boot tramped heavily on a paper sack of sugar, splitting it open, and then Remsberg was roughly fending him aside.

"Leave it! I will take care of this." Remsberg was stooped over and reaching out as Shiffley straightened suddenly and kicked him idly in the right temple.

Momentarily stunned, he saw Max Fass's spindly figure poised above him as he tried to raise himself. The gun in Fass's fist swished down at him in a glittering arc. He groaned and collapsed across the empty gunny sack. Everything went black.

Abby Ellsworth was putting on her hat, primping before a mirror in back of the counter, when John Remsberg walked into Ellsworth's Mercantile for the second time in one day. An austere-looking man in his middle years stood behind the counter near her, and from just a passing glance Remsberg knew this must be her father. Clayton Ellsworth had the same fine, delicately boned features, the same smoky swirls in his granite-cool eyes.

Abby caught his reflection in the mirror as he shuffled hesitantly up to the counter, and as she spun around and their eyes met, color surged into the faces at the same instant.

"Why—Mr. Remsberg! This—this visit is sooner than I had expected."

Embarrassment at her mistake sank deeper color into his high cheekbones. "I . . . I do not make a visit," he blurted awkwardly. "I have come to buy more things."

"Oh! I see." Her voice chilled faintly before she caught herself and hastily erased the note of pique from it. "You forgot some items. And I judged you for the kind who never forgets anything."

"I did not forget the items."

"But you just said—"

He interrupted humbly: "Forgive me that I do not make it clear. There was out at my place a little . . . fuss. You could perhaps credit me for the same order again—no?"

A startled look crossed her face, then shock spread fully over it as she noticed the bruised swelling at his right temple, where Dan Shiffley's spur had raked it open.

"You were hurt!" she exclaimed.

"It is nothing."

"Who did this, John?" His given name burst from her before she was aware of it. She covered her confusion by angrily shaking her head. "If you had taken my advice and worn a gun, this would not have happened."

"A gun?" He looked at her doggedly. "A gun I would forget I had."

"Who did this? Who did it?" she demanded tensely.

He told her about Shiffley and Fass, ending it lamely: "Next time I will be prepared for such monkey business. I would have invited them in for a *Klatsch*. A neighborly call, I am thinking, when I see them come into my dooryard."

"A neighborly call! And they beat you up and destroyed your supplies!" Abby Ellsworth bristled. "I've heard of those sneaking carpetbaggers! Cheap Northern trash! I—" She stopped suddenly, a furious blush mantling her cheeks. "I'm sorry," she said. "I didn't mean to—"

"It is all right. We are all under the same flag now."

She swung abruptly, her glance going to where Clayton Ellsworth stood, his eyes narrowed and dour, shuttling between them.

"Father, this is John Remsberg. You knew that he was taking over the old Remsberg place."

"I knew that, yes. I have also heard talk in town about Mr. Remsberg that has not been favorable."

"You have heard nothing but a sly whispering campaign spawned in some dirty saloon! That has nothing to do with this. Credit for a few staples."

"I also overheard your conversation with him just now," replied Clayton Ellsworth coldly. "What happened out there today at his ranch can happen again. A storekeeper cannot afford to pour molasses into a leaky barrel."

"But, Father! This is not a leaky barrel. Mr. Remsberg owns a ranch. He is not a . . . a saddle tramp!"

"I did not say that he was. But if slander has been spoken against him, he cannot honorably ignore it."

"Is 'Peaceful' a slanderous word, Father?"

"It is, when spoken with intent to defame."

"It is not when spoken by a vicious little clique of drunkards and town riffraff who have not the courage to come out and speak it to his face! Mr. Remsberg may not have fought on our side in the war, but he was a soldier. He is not a coward! He—"

John Remsberg's voice trembled out across her words. "It is no matter. Thank you. I will try at the Eagle Mercantile." And he turned to go.

A slow comprehension broke in Clayton Ellsworth's eyes as Abby spun around, facing him. "Father," she demanded fiercely, "have you ever lost a single dollar from credit I have written for this store?"

"Why—why no, Abby. I don't guess I have. But—"

"You have not and you will not! Anyway, it is not the money you are concerned about—or need to be!"

Abby's voice shook. Clayton Ellsworth stared with a numbed look at her flashing eyes, at the sudden pallor skirting the frail line of her mouth. She swished around, and the impelling vehemence of her voice halted John Remsberg just as he reached the door.

"Mr. Remsberg! Wait!"

Regularly, after that, two nights each week, John Remsberg drove in to Bandera to see Abby Ellsworth. The fact was accepted in town now. Abby Ellsworth and the carpetbagger who had inherited Gus Remsberg's old siwash outfit were goin' steady. Clayton Ellsworth's daughter—the younger, sassy one. Clayton's only boy had died of a Federal bullet at Bull Run. One of the first to volunteer. And now Miss Abby, apple of the old man's eyes, tarry-hootin' around with a damn blue-belly. Be a scandal, surer than hellfire, if a match come of it.

The town gossip. The sly winks and covert whisperings. They ignored it all. They were too busy with each other, moving alone and uncaring in a world apart, and content just to hold their dream.

After a long day's work out in the brasada John Remsberg was usually exhausted, yet the satisfaction he derived in making the ten-mile drive into town and reporting his progress to Abby more than compensated him for the hardship the trip entailed. He had better than threescore of cows put in his iron now, and penned up in a boxed canyon, a mile from the house. Sentimentally he had chosen 7T6 as his brand—the year in which he would take Abby for his bride and start his new life in this new and wonderful land.

With the last of his savings, money he had kept cached under a loose board in his kitchen floor, he had bought a good rope horse and a pair of home-tanned *armitas,* and while he had not yet become a skilled rider he had quickly caught on to the knack of throwing a rope, and the muscles in his corded arms and anvil-thick shoulders were strong as a bull's.

He had never been to her home. Their meeting place was the dingy lobby of the hotel, and from there they took long walks together, sometimes strolling far out of town, often filled with chatter and as often not, and as content when they were silent as when they talked. Then one night she stopped and looked straight at him. "You have not met my older sister. Saturday I want you to call on me at home."

To pay his call, he put on the only store-bought suit he had. And in the Ellsworths' fine front parlor he sat stiff and awkward on the horsehair sofa beside her, unused to such elegance and feeling confused and uneasy in spite of her efforts to put him at ease.

Abby's older sister, Tilda, who had babied her from the time she was ten, when their mother had died, finally came in to be introduced, a prim, severe-looking young woman with a tight-drawn mouth and eyes that seemed to skim over John Remsberg in unspoken derogation. With grudging clemency she went through the formality of sipping a cup of tea with them, then quickly excused herself. Clayton Ellsworth did not make even this pretense of hospitality. Coat and hat across his arm, he accorded John Remsberg a brusque nod as he passed through the room, saying, "Good evening, sir," and then marched on stiffly to the door.

Watching Abby sitting erectly beside him, in hurt dignity, John Remsberg felt her misery more than he did his own. He stood abruptly.

"I told you it would not work out. They do not want me in this house, Abby."

With an angry gesture, Abby shook out her skirt and rose. "Then they do not want me here, either."

John Remsberg's big hand motioned over the richly appointed room. "I cannot give you fine things like this, Abby."

Her vehemence startled him. "John Remsberg, you are a fool!"

"I am not welcome here, Abby. I will not come again."

"You will not have to."

"It is not much I can offer you."

"It is enough that I will have you, John."

A week later they were quietly married in the little Baptist parsonage on lower Main Street. The Reverend Adam Doan and his wife were the only witnesses.

He improved his holding pen and learned to throw a hoolihan, and time like a great wheel slowly ground its grist of days, and his herd increased, and Abby was going to have a baby. It was so. Not for months yet, but the doctor in Bandera had assured them. He prayed it would be a boy. A son and heir for the greatness of what he would someday build here. His dream stretched in bigness. An empire of golden hides and ivory horns. Great herds with his 7T6 branded on each brute's flank, and streaming northward in a never-ending tide. In this vast land the imagination spilled over, for there was no bottom to its wellsprings.

He grew lean and saddle-hammered from his work in the brasada, and there were upwards of a hundred and fifty cows in his pen now. He could get two, maybe three dollars a head for these, in Bandera. He would take it. He would drive to town soon, with Abby, and make the necessary arrangements. With three hundred dollars in his pocket—*ja,* maybe more!—he would buy her a fine present. And build another room on the house. *Ja, ja.* Time did not stand still. Soon they would be needing it.

But he was not always happy coming in at dusk, exhausted from a hard day working the brush, even though Abby usually was at the door to meet him, her arms often flour-powdered from baking, and her greeting kiss was something he looked forward to the whole day through. He noticed that she had seemed strangely quiet and preoccupied of late, and this worried him. Women in a delicate condition were prone to the vapors, he knew. It could be that. Or it could be that she was pining for the softer, easier life that she had left behind her, in Bandera.

With a few of the personal belongings that she brought here from her home, she had titivated up their bedroom until it seemed almost as pretentious as a room in Clayton Ellsworth's big house in town. There was an old walnut highboy, with curved brass handles which she assiduously polished every day; a huge mirror framed in cherry wood, and a dainty cherry-wood chair, with legs so thin and fine that he had never dared sit in it; and a great walnut four-poster bed, so wide that it left only a narrow space on one side of the small room, to come in to it.

By comparison, the rough-hewn furniture that August Remsberg had made for the living room looked poor and shabby. When the bedroom door was open the mirror reflected the living room's drabness, and John Remsberg took an aversion to it, since it seemed to rebuke him for the littleness of what he had been able to give her, in contrast to the bigness of his dream.

Then one night when they were in the kitchen, finishing supper, he learned what was troubling her—not her condition, nor a yearning for geegaws and fripperies beyond their present means, but simply concern over him.

"John," she said out of a clear sky while he sat packing his pipe and watching the lamplight play over the frail planes of her face, "it is too quiet. I have been expecting something to happen, and it has not."

"Something to happen?" He knew immediately what she was driving at. He did not want her to know that he knew. "*Ja.* It has been quiet. And peaceful." He held a match poised, looking at her. "But you do not call it something happening when we have one hundred and fifty cows in our holding pen?"

"You know what I am talking about, John Remsberg!"

He scratched the match alight and applied it to the charred bowl of his meerschaum, puffing a moment before answering: "*Ja.* You are talking of Dan Shiffley. That is finished. There is no more trouble."

"I know that shirt-tail Shiffley clan! And I think you should carry a gun."

He sighed, relaxing in his chair. "You are very beautiful when you look so serious, *Liebchen.*"

"Do not put me off with sweet talk!"

"There is a rifle in the house."

"A blunderbuss, you mean! You should wear a side arm. It won't mean you are looking for trouble. Just that you'll be ready, if it should come."

"Fiddle-faddle."

"Don't you fiddle-faddle me! You cannot let yourself be run over, John. Or let anyone think you can be."

"No one is going to run over me, *Liebchen.*"

"We are just out of coffee." Abruptly, Abby rose and began clearing the table. "Tomorrow you can drive me to town in the buckboard. And if you will not buy a gun, I will buy one for you."

"Tomorrow is fine. Tomorrow while you buy your coffee and guns, I will see the cattle buyer, Estes Trenholm. Three hundred dollars we will have, Abby. We will shoot up the town to-gether—*nein?*"

She did not answer him. It was their first quarrel.

All during their drive to town the next morning Abby sat beside him withdrawn and silent, and their quarrel was still unresolved when they arrived finally at the Eagle Mercantile, where, since Abby's estrangement from her family, they had done what little trading had been necessary for them. But the real blow had not fallen until half an hour later, after he had talked with Estes Trenholm in the lobby of Huffmeyer's Hotel and afterward had rushed across the street to the Bandera county clerk's office, spurred by a wild hope that the cattle buyer might have been mistaken in what he had told him. Trenholm had not been mistaken.

In the county clerk's office he could feel his heart's dull, panicked hacking against his ribs as he stared at the clerk's smugly calm face.

"You . . . you are sure of this?" he blurted out tensely. "There is . . . no chance of mistake?"

"We don't make that kind of mistake here, mister. There it is —right in the book." The clerk jabbed his pencil at an inked notation in the ledger opened before him. "Brand 7T6—registered in the name of one Max Fass." He thumped the ledger shut. "Looks like you ain't got no cattle, mister—till you ketch you some more. Even a greener should savvy you can't legally claim a brand in this county till it's recorded."

John Remsberg wheeled slowly and stumbled out of the office. Outside he stood tracked for a long moment on the boardwalk, staring around him with the vacantly disconcerted look of a man suddenly realizing that he has become lost. Finally, lurching around, he broke distractedly into a long-gaited stride, heading downstreet.

His brain whirled. He had been played upon for a fool, and a fool he was. A *Dumnkopf,* unworthy to possess a ranch, or a wife like Abby. Had not she warned him, again and again? But even Abby had taken it for granted he must be aware of this simple, commonly known rule about registering brands. Who but a dolt like himself would not have known about it? And last night, when she had again warned him against Shiffley, what had he done but strut before her like a stupid jackass and make a joke of her advice!

Ja, it was his own stupid pride and conceit that had brought him to this. And because he was such a simpleton this herd he had toiled so hard to collect now belonged legally to Max Fass. Or to Fass and Shiffley, since they were undoubtedly in on this deal together. No doubt they had already driven the gather to their own pens. And there was not a thing he could do about it. With a sinking despair, he remembered the clerk's words. *Looks like you ain't got no cattle, mister—till you ketch you some more.* How would he ever be able to face Abby—now?

I cannot, he thought miserably. *I cannot do it.* He lost all awareness of time and was far out of town when he awoke suddenly to the fact that he had been walking steadily for almost an hour. He turned and started back.

There was no prelude to it. He was on lower Main Street and passing the Steamboat Saloon when the batwings swung open

and there was Dan Shiffley. Without a word he walked up to
Shiffley and struck him across the face. Shiffley's eyes stretched
in started recognition as he made a bull-like rush at him, but the
fight did not last long. His pent-up fury had needed this outlet
and his final cudgeling blow belted Shiffley up off his feet.

There was a nebulousness and unreality to the rest of it. The
blurred sea of faces circled around him. Shiffley blundering to
his feet, and the bloody pincers of his mouth opening to gust
the savage, wheezed-out words.

"All right, damn you, all right! Now you get a gun or be out
of town by noon."

The sea of faces becoming a wall, a wall of prejudice and
hostility shutting off the sun and sky and the dream he had
brought to this harsh raw land. John Remsberg rammed his
knotted shoulders against the wall and it broke. He began walking away from it. He knew it was still there, re-forming, behind him. He knew there was one way to break it, permanently.
Only one.

The owner of the hardware store had let in the first ray of
light. As he had stood at the counter, buckling on the new, shiny
Walker pistol, the storekeeper told him: "Punch it at him fast,
mister. Dan Shiffley's bad medicine. He's quick on the pull."

The first ray . . . Was it the beginning of full, clear light?
The first breach in the wall? Outside the store, under its wooden
awning, Remsberg heaved a sigh. Until he had asked to look
at guns, the storekeeper had been as aloof and withdrawn toward him as those others had been earlier, in front of the
Steamboat. With his intentions made clear, a constrained, grudging kind of friendliness had come over the man. It was wrong.
Ironically, stupidly wrong that his mere strapping on of a gun
belt should have made this difference.

Absently Remsberg's hand stoked down against the unfamiliar
weight of the holster sagging from his hip. But wasn't there,
perhaps, a degree of rightness in it, too? No one could deny the
wrongness of the method. But did not the method stem from
necessity?

And Remsberg felt, now, that he had found his answer to that. *Progress is slow,* he thought, *and where the law is weak, men must be strong. Custom is not changed by a few, or in a day.*

He moved out from the shelter of the awning, sensitive to a sudden preternatural quiet that seemed to have descended upon the town. The boardwalks were deserted, buckboards and spring wagons stood unattended at the hitch rails. And this was Saturday. Something portentous and unnatural about it pulled at Remsberg's taut nerves.

The word has gone out, he thought somberly. And suddenly it hit him. The stillness was not complete. Behind it lay a muted overtone, a vague humming sound, like the drone of voices in a theater before the curtain rises and the play begins. And then he noticed the pulled-back window curtains, the eyes peering at him from shadowy doorways. Oddly, though, the eyes seemed neither friendly nor unfriendly but only stiffly, curiously expectant.

Unconsciously his pace had adjusted to the slow, stalking gait of a hunter's, and at this moment he remembered the hardware merchant's words, and an odd feeling of stimulation rose in him. *Punch it at him fast, mister.* There had been a ring of sincerity in the man's voice; maybe there were others who felt as he did. Maybe, today, he did not walk alone. . . .

He caught a sharp ammonia reek as he was passing Neubauer's Livery and he was just beyond it when the voice floated after him from the wide stable doorway.

"He's still down at the Steamboat. Walk up on him easy, Yank."

He did not look back, but a sudden warm tightness tingled in his throat as he paced on, swallowing vainly against it. And then his belly plunged coldly. Forward a block, sharp noon sunlight glinted on the brass ship's bell hanging above the doorway of the Steamboat Saloon. And two doors below, on the opposite side of the street, the white-painted false front of Ellsworth's Mercantile canted its low wooden awning out over the boardwalk.

Abby, thought Remsberg. *Is she there—in the store?* And then he remembered, and relief was like a strong, warming drink in his belly. Abby had not been to the store or seen her father since the day of their marriage.

His pace slowed. He was less than a hundred yards from the Steamboat now. Abby. His *Süssliebchen*. So little he had been able to do for her. And now—a few months only—and the baby would come. Of that he must not think. A boy. A boy it must be. He had prayed for that. He had talked solemnly, with God. So that if anything happened to him, now . . .

Now! Now it would be, or it would not be. Like walking out of a dark cave against a tearing wind. It grabs your breath. Your lungs suddenly are dry and empty.

The Steamboat's batwings swung open and flapped shut behind Dan Shiffley. His chilly eyes accosted Remsberg's. He was smoothing a finished cigarette between his fingers and as Remsberg halted he did a disdainful thing. He scratched a match against his black whipcord breeches and idly touched its flame to the tip of the cigarette.

Remsberg sensed a wrongness in the picture. Shiffley was bluffing. He could not feel that sure. The range. That must be it. The range was not right yet. Shiffley was trying to panic him into a fast draw, into making a wild first shot. Then . . .

A cramping numbness was in Remsberg's legs as he started moving them again. He remembered that feeling. At Sharpsburg. The bridge over Antietam Creek. Elements of General Toombs's 2nd and 20th Georgia Regiments had held it. Warren's Brigade was ordered to cross. And under deadly enfilading fire to those Rebel sharpshooters they had crossed. And on legs that had felt like brittle sticks, he, John Remsberg, had crossed. . . .

"Don't slow down, Dutch!" Shiffley's voice carried a jeering vehemence, reaching him. "You got sand enough in your craw, keep a-comin'."

It was a trick. Shiffley was egging him on. Trying deliberately to provoke him into a blunder. But how much longer could Shiffley wait?

Remsberg moved on, doling each step, feeling the pressure within him now, like a slowly tightening spring. He estimated sixty feet, fifty. Then forty.

Shiffley spat the cigarette from his mouth. He still did not move.

Suddenly the odd prescient feeling in Remsberg sharpened. Something about Shiffley's studied unconcern struck a false note. Remsberg halted.

And at that moment the shot blared. *Not from Shiffley's gun.* The realization rang a warning in Remsberg. *Don't turn. Don't turn!* The vital split-second advantage that should have been Shiffley's tipped in Remsberg's favor. Shiffley's eyes were stretched in a look of shocked disbelief staring past Remsberg and as he recovered to start his draw Remsberg cleared leather first and fired.

The mighty, walloping report bounced between the street's false fronts and skirled away in a fading rataplan of echoes. Shiffley had the appearance of a man vaguely preoccupied by a need to sit down suddenly. He took a squatting position as his knees buckled, holding on to his belly. And as he rocked backward and down, he gave the grotesque impression of a person who has had a chair abruptly drawn from under him.

Remsberg turned. All along Main, doors were opening and people were pouring into the street. Already a sizable crowd had gathered in front of Ellsworth's Mercantile, and Remsberg stared vacantly at it for a long moment before suddenly recognizing Clayton Ellsworth's tall, spare figure standing at its forefront. Shock froze his eyes then. A big Walker pistol hung slackly in Ellsworth's right hand, and as Remsberg swung his head, following the storekeeper's fixed forward gaze, he abruptly went rigid.

The body lay sprawled on the boardwalk in front of Buckley's saddle shop, twenty feet from the Mercantile. Max Fass's head dangled over the walk's high edge, his skinny arms outthrust like those of a swimmer arrested in the midst of a breast stroke. The gun he had never come to fire lay in the gutter beneath his right hand, glittering diamondlike in the bright sunlight.

Fass! Clayton Ellsworth had shot Fass! Light burst through the fogginess in Remsberg's brain as he stared at the crumpled body. Now, like the final piece of a picture puzzle falling into place, it was all complete for him. While Shiffley had been baiting him on, from in front of the Steamboat, Fass had been moving stealthily out of that alley between the stores, intending to ambush him. And Ellsworth had seen him. That one shot he had heard. The shot that had brought the look of panic in Dan Shiffley's eyes. Shiffley had been faced toward Fass. He had seen it happen. And the shock had slowed his draw.

Remsberg's breath caught. He saw a jostling movement in the crowd. Then Abby had fought her way through it and was running toward him. When she was in his arms, his throat was too tight for words as she hugged him fiercely to her. He stroked her tumbled hair and at last got through the tightness to murmur, *"Liebchen,"* feeling a giddy whirling in his head as she kept sobbing his name and punched her cheek deeper into the pit of his shoulder.

He had, at first, only a remote awareness of the other voice.

". . . like to have sprained my wrist, gettin' the gun away from her. Ellsworth women always were a notional lot. Don't guess there's any way to cure 'em, either, except switch their bottoms when there's a needin' to."

Dazedly, Remsberg looked up and saw Clayton Ellsworth. "What . . . what was that? I am sorry. I did not hear—"

The storekeeper's thin, pinched mouth relaxed slowly in a grin.

"You better never mind that part of it." The grin widened as John Remsberg stared down at the knotty fingers splayed out in front of him. "Shake hands, son," Clayton Ellsworth said. "And welcome to Texas."

God Help the Vigilantes!

BY FRANK C. ROBERTSON

It is not a common concept, but true, nonetheless, that it was not only men and events which made Western settlement possible. Behind those men and events, motivating and directing them, were certain beliefs—certain convictions in terms of ethics, morality, and law— which stamped themselves as surely upon the land as upon the character and nature of its people. One of these convictions—a view of social necessity as hard to justify today as it was among the Vigilantes of Alder Gulch or San Francisco—was that in the face of anarchy and the collapse of formal law, citizens had not only the right but the moral obligation to take the responsibilities and duties of the law upon themselves, even if by illegal means. Even in extremes of necessity enforced by the most brutal and rapacious disorder, the decision to take men's lives without benefit of duly constituted court and jury must surely have been one of the most difficult free men have ever faced.

—T.W.B.

THE most peaceful hour of the whole day in Gold Reef was between sundown and dark. The clamor of the day's business had abated somewhat, while the drunken, hilarious revelry of the boom town's night life had not yet begun. It was at this hour that Captain Jed Hawley liked to walk the drab, dirty, but to him exciting main street with his young wife, Jolene.

Like every other true pioneer, the captain professed the gift of prophecy—so far as his own town was concerned. "Someday, my sweet," he said, "she'll be the Chicago of the West."

His pretty wife smiled. "In five years, after the gold is all taken out, you'll be saying the same thing about some other town."

The captain looked down at her and grinned. He was older than she; a good twelve years, to be exact. He was thirty-five and she twenty-three. Like many of his kind, he had been too busy getting his start to think of marriage, until frost began to show in his sideburns. He was humbly, devoutly grateful that a girl like Jolene had found in him enough to cause her to risk her future in his hands. He was accustomed to being accepted as a leader among men, but he would never be able to get over the miracle of Jolene's love.

There was a burden on his mind now which he feared his wife half guessed. It made him artificially cheerful as he pointed out the new, raw, unpainted false-fronted buildings as positive proof that fulfillment of his favorite prophecy was already unfolding before their eyes. Not the least source of his pride was that Hawley's Livery and Feed Store boasted the highest false front in town, and that the corrals back of the stable were filled with the finest horses in all the Territory; and, further, that he personally enjoyed the nearly unique reputation of an honest horse trader.

Their walk took them down the main street to the banks of the turgid little creek, thick and yellow with tailings from the placer diggings above. They continued along a winding trail up the side of a hill, through a thicket of sweet-smelling wild honeysuckle, to the top of a knoll which commanded a view of the entire squalid little town of five thousand people. Mostly men.

As he pointed out the sure and certain signs of permanent growth, Jolene clung to his arm and regarded his earnest face with secret, inner amusement of a mother for an overenthusiastic child. She loved and respected him, and gloried in the esteem in which he was held by other men.

He fell silent.

"What's the matter, Jed?" she asked softly.

"Matter? Why, nothing at all. Everything is going great. I've got a good business and a—"

"I know. You'll end the recital, 'a loving wife.' But you won't tell me why you're worried; why you stay away from home, night after night, and why you sometimes come home with your face as gray and shocked as though you had seen a ghost, and your hands trembling."

"You imagine things."

"There have been four men hanged at different times here in the last three months, Jed. Each time it was on a night when you didn't get home until daybreak."

"You don't understand about these things, Jolene. Any mining camp attracts reckless and lawless characters like honey does flies. There's not much law except such as we ourselves make. If we didn't do something, decent women like you wouldn't be safe on the streets; honest men wouldn't be able to even carry on their business. It's difficult enough, now."

"Then you are a Vigilante."

He nodded gravely, his eyes screwed down as if in pain. "It's necessary. I wish I could make you understand. Most of these badmen are mere boys. It's not easy to take the poor, profane, blustering young desperadoes out to a tree, knowing that nine times out of ten they'll crack at the last minute, grab your knees if they can and beg you to let them live, and then—then—"

Tears stood in Jolene's eyes as she watched the quivering of his silky, magnificent beard.

"You don't have to do it, Jed. Let somebody else—"

"I *do* have to do it. This is something no decent man can shirk. God knows I didn't want to. I tried to keep in the background, but you know I was a captain of militia in the Indian trouble. I was the only one who had ever commanded men."

He gazed at her miserably. It was seldom he spoke to her of his military experience. She knew that he disliked being called "captain."

"Then you are," she said presently, "the leader."

"I told you they forced it onto me," he growled, like a goaded grizzly.

Her slim white hand touched his arm. "I know, dear. I trust

you. It's just that I couldn't bear to have anything happen to you. Some of these outlaws have friends. If they knew it was you—"

"Don't worry about that. Every Vigilante is pledged to secrecy. I shouldn't have told you. Besides, out here, every man has to face a certain amount of danger, take his chances."

It wasn't exactly what she had meant. She understood the physical danger he must face, and she wouldn't shrink from it, any more than he would. But this sort of thing could do more than kill a man; it could kill his soul and leave his body living. Under his terse, sometimes hard mannerisms she knew that he was as sensitive to emotions as he was indifferent to physical pain.

The ghosts of these hanged young outlaws would live with him, and he wasn't the sort of man who could live with ghosts. She tried to tell him that.

"Let's go back," she said finally.

At the foot of the winding trail they met another couple. It dismayed Jolene a little to see the tentative start which Jed made toward his gun. But his hand didn't quite touch the weapon, and he smiled. He was wonderfully handsome when he used that rare smile. At other times he was rather common looking, a stockily built man with keen blue eyes which could hold the gaze of another as if fixed there on the tines of an invisible fork. In contrast with the handsome, well-dressed, black-eyed, smiling man who confronted them, he looked plain and drab.

"Jed! Jed Hawley! So this is where you take that captivating wife of yours every evening? Mrs. Hawley, ma'am, I've been intending to challenge your husband to a duel soon unless he introduced me."

Jolene warmed to the man's pleasant manners at once. "I'm sure he will now," she smiled.

"If you'll present the lady on your arm," Jed said.

"And I am proud to do so! Captain and Mrs. Hawley—my wife."

Jolene grasped the hand of the young girl eagerly. She was not over nineteen. "Delighted to know you, my dear, even if I still don't know your name."

"This is Jack Marlo, Jolene," Jed said.

Marlo bowed low. "I can't tell you how happy I am to have you two girls know each other. Isabel is new to this country, and I know you'll be kind to her. We were married at Fort Benton only three weeks ago. Have been back only two or three days."

"I'll be glad to do anything for Mrs. Marlo that I can."

"I'll be grateful," Isabel Marlo said appealingly. She was a small girl, plump and pretty as a young guinea hen, with wide, questioning eyes and a trembly, uncertain sort of smile.

They chatted a few minutes, and Jolene was pleased to note the reserve in her husband's stern manner thaw like a snowbank in the embrace of a spring chinook.

After leaving the Marlos, they were almost home before either spoke. Jolene had learned when not to break in on her husband's meditations.

"I can't believe it!" he broke out. "Jack Marlo marrying a girl like that."

"Why? What do you know about him?" Jolene asked eagerly.

"I've known Jack a long time," he said slowly. "We met when we were coming West up the Missouri River for the first time—little more than kids. The first thing the cuss did was save my life when I fell off the boat and got tangled in the towrope."

"Oh!"

"We hunted buffalo together and fought Indians together. Seems like we bump into each other almost every place we go."

"But what does he do?" Jolene asked.

He shook his head dumbly. He would have given half he owned to have been able to answer. Four road agents had been hanged by the Vigilantes at Gold Reef, but Captain Jed Hawley and many of his associates felt the ones they had picked up were only lone wolves and that the real core of outlaw activity had not been touched. They were working to uncover that core, and when they did succeed, Jed feared that Jack Marlo would be uncovered, too, like a bright green tiger beetle under a chip.

In three days the two girls were fast friends. Isabel, more than a little frightened by the noisy life of the mining town, spent the greater part of her time with Jolene at the Hawleys' neat four-room cabin.

As the days wore on, Jolene grew worried over the harried expression on Isabel's face. The girl was wildly in love with Jack Marlo but she was not happy. At last Jolene got it out of her that night after night she lay sleeplessly waiting for the footsteps of her husband, who frequently failed to show up before noon the next day.

Jolene spoke to Jed about it. There had been no more hangings, and the somber expression on his face was lifting almost imperceptibly.

"Reckon she's just not eatin' her oats," Jed gave the horseman's stock answer for trouble.

"This is serious, Jed. Isabel isn't like the rest of us here. She's soft. You don't need to tell me why Jack stays away so many nights, but isn't there any chance at all that it will soon be over? That he'll be with her more often?"

"All I can say is," Jed answered, "I sure hope so."

The next day a stage, carrying a pool of forty thousand dollars in gold sent out by Gold Reef merchants was held up and robbed, and the shotgun messenger wounded. The following morning Jed and a man named Wade Cook met Jack Marlo just as he was turning into a saloon in which he owned a half interest. Marlo invited them in to have a drink, including Cook merely because he happened to be with Jed. Cook, a small man with close-cropped red hair that would never stay combed, had a hatchet face, and small, darting eyes that seemed to be on an eternal quest for another man's thoughts, so that he could be on the popular side. He owned a sawmill on the outskirts of town. Because the fellow was always pretending to be bigger than his stature as a citizen warranted, Jed despised him no less than did Marlo, although he concealed his dislike better.

Jed refused a drink but lingered for a moment on the sidewalk. "Bad business, that holdup yesterday, Jack," he said.

"Wasn't it? Still, sending a lone shotgun guard out on a stage loaded like that was murder itself. The guard was lucky. What can one or two men do against fifteen or twenty road agents?"

"Sooner or later the road agents will find themselves on the small end of the horn, and when they do there is only one place they can wind up."

"You bet you're right," Cook exclaimed. "The end of a rope, that's the place for 'em. How I'd like to see every one of them kick and dangle."

Jed said slowly, "I wouldn't."

"I suspect that one road agent who didn't lose his nerve could scare the waddin' out of any bunch of Vigilantes who ever met in a dark room and talked in whispers," Jack Marlo said testily.

Cook glanced eagerly at Jed.

"I doubt that, Jack," Jed said. "Anyway, if I was a road agent, I wouldn't bank on it."

"Well, maybe I wouldn't, either," Marlo admitted.

"There's one funny thing about that holdup," Jed said slowly. "All the details of the shipment were guarded. There hasn't been a stickup for over three months, yet the road agents picked the only lucky day."

"Does seem funny," said Marlo. "I lost a few hundred dollars myself."

Only five days later came the break Jed Hawley half wanted and half dreaded. He was working around his livery stable when a Dutchman named Herzog, whom he knew slightly, galloped in on a nearly exhausted horse. Jed knew the man had a mining claim on one of the small creeks heading around Horse Prairie.

"Captain! Captain, I got news for you!" The man flung himself from the lathered horse. "Nat Brown and his boy haff been murdered."

"What!" Jed gasped. It was incredible that a man so well

known as Brown should be murdered. With his sixteen-year-old
son, Brown had run a horse ranch on Horse Prairie for two
years. That made him an old settler. He was known to everybody.

"Dot is right," Herzog declared. "Und I see who done it."

"You saw the murder?"

"Nod exactly. I am fresh oud of baking powder und I go over
to Nat Brown's to borrow some. I am nearly dere when I hear
shots. I see two men run from de corral to de house. I stay
vere I am. Few minutes later they run oud again and git on
their horses. As dey leaf they ride close to the brush vhere I
am hid. I see them goot. Dey are Dave Reeder und Slim Sheets.
Vhen I reach de corral I find Nat und his boy bot' dead. Nat is
shot in de back und de boy in de head."

A little questioning enabled Jed to get the complete picture.
Nat Brown had recently sold a large number of horses. The two
road agents had stayed all night with him, lured him and his
son out to the corral after breakfast, and catching them off guard,
had murdered them both. Only for the accident of the Dutchman being out of baking powder, the identity of the slayers
would never have been known.

"All right, Herzog," Jed said. "Get yourself something to eat.
I'll take care of your horse. Say nothing to anybody about this,
but come back here after dark."

A little careful inquiry revealed Dave Reeder and Slim
Sheets had been staying at the isolated ranch of a man named
Bud Wilson. A few whispered words were passed around, and
Captain Jed went home to inform Jolene that he was going to
be gone all night. He dreaded the telling, but it had to be done.

"Something to do with the stage robbery, I suppose," she
said.

"Maybe. Anyway, it has to do with the murder of a good
citizen and an innocent boy. They were shot down without a
chance."

"Jed, why doesn't the law handle it?"

"Whenever a man we suspect of being a road agent is arrested by the county officers, he is let go. They have crooked

lawyers, their friends intimidate jurymen—and we're none too sure of the officers themselves. If we could trust them, God knows we wouldn't take the law into our own hands."

"I can't believe things are as bad as you say. Why don't you let the law handle this—just once?" Jolene pleaded.

"My dear, you don't understand. There is a crime ring. This may be the only chance we'll ever have to break it. If we sent out Jim Smith, the local deputy sheriff, and he happened to be a friend of theirs, we'd be responsible for murders yet to come."

"I've seen Jim Smith often. He's a friend of Jack Marlo's. He doesn't seem like an outlaw to me," she cried heatedly.

He thought a great deal about Jolene in ensuing hours as he rode at the head of twenty-odd grim-visaged Vigilantes on the thirty-mile ride to Wilson's ranch. But once there he had no time for anything but the business at hand.

They arrived an hour before daybreak. There were two small log buildings, a cabin and a stable, with a corral in front of the latter. Three saddles by the corral gate told them the men were there.

Captain Jed posted his men about the buildings and gave them final instructions. "Don't shoot unless you have to. We want these men alive."

He took his own position at the end of the stable, just out of sight of the log house.

Half an hour later dawn smoke began to curl up from the roof of the cabin. Bud Wilson came to the door and went back. Soon the tantalizing odor of frying bacon and boiling coffee reached the nostrils of the hungry men outside. It was cold, waiting. The captain pressed his numbed hands between his arms and ribs to warm them.

The sun had just topped the timber-crested hills to the east when three men came out to the corral. Wilson's two visitors were indeed the men they sought. Captain Jed stepped from behind the stable, revolver in hand.

"Throw up your hands, boys," he ordered quietly. "You're surrounded and it will do you no good to resist."

"The Vigilantes!" Slim Sheets exclaimed, but the hands of all three men shot skyward. Captain Jed's concealed men came forward to form a close-packed ring around the outlaws.

"What the devil is this?" Bud Wilson demanded.

"We're not sure about you, Wilson, but we want Reeder and Sheets for the murder of Nat Brown and his boy," Jed told them in a cold, expressionless voice.

Their indignant denials subsided when confronted by Herzog. They were frontiersmen and they knew what to expect.

"All we ask is a fair trial at the county seat," Dave Reeder said.

"You'll get a fair trial—here," Captain Jed told them. "It's going on right now."

Twenty minutes from the time the outlaws left the cabin, Reeder and Sheets were unanimously found guilty and sentenced to death. Bud Wilson was given two hours to get over the Continental Divide, with the assurance of certain death if he tried to tarry. The court of justice held its session in front of a fire; the long wait had chilled the Vigilantes.

"You men are part of an organization," Captain Jed told the two condemned to death. "Nothing you can say will help your case, but you would die easier if you would expose the men who recruit boys like you to do murder. One murder prevented might help atone for the ones you've committed."

"You go to hell!" Dave Reeder growled.

"You got the same feelings, Slim?" the captain asked. "You haven't got much time to square things."

"Will you let me write a letter to my father?" Sheets requested. He was as white as the articles which his name represented.

"If you make it fast."

It wasn't the first time Jed had seen hardened young devils scrawling out maudlin messages through their tears to loved ones whose names they had disgraced. He was not greatly surprised when Slim Sheets, half through his letter, suddenly dropped his head to his arms and began to sob.

Half an hour later the Vigilantes had Slim's confession, with the names of all the officers and members of the infamous organization to which he belonged. To Slim had been given the high-sounding title of corresponding secretary. His last performance was a roll call of death, for which his own reward was the boon of being hanged ahead of Dave Reeder.

Listed on the paper, high among the officials of the road agents' band, was the name "Jack Marlo, messenger."

After the hanging, the Vigilantes waited for their leader to speak. While they thought he was pondering the next move, he was pushing against a fog of befuddling bewilderment, as though it were something that could be lifted by sheer will power. But the fog continued to ooze through the thrusting fingers of his mind.

Jack Marlo had been the most intimate friend he had ever had. Now, to make things worse, Jack's wife was his wife's best friend. During the two months he had known her, Jed himself had become very fond of Isabel. Sometimes he had caught her paying him a silent tribute with her eyes in a way that embarrassed him.

Now he had to go back and hang Jack Marlo and make Isabel, that charming, helpless, pathetic little girl wife, a widow.

He couldn't resign from the Vigilantes. That had been part of the solemn oath these honest men had taken when they pledged themselves to rid the country of lawlessness. Each man had agreed that his own life should be forfeit should he fail in his duty.

Fear of consequences, however, had never bothered the captain. He had joined the Vigilantes because of a firm conviction that it was the only way to establish the ordered system of society which respectable people had to have. The violent, exuberant selfishness of a raw country was not susceptible to the orderly processes of organized government. Too many times he had seen timid or conniving officials stand aside to let swaggering gunmen and road agents have their way. He had joined the Gold Reef Vigilantes only when he saw this very thing happening before his eyes.

Wade Cook spoke up. "There's four of the leaders livin' right in Gold Reef. Why don't we hustle back there and hang 'em before they can get away?" His smallish eyes danced with the pleasure of anticipation. Jed had been sickened by the sadistic enjoyment the man had taken in the hanging of Sheets and Reeder.

Jed had to speak. "We've got sixteen names on our list," he said slowly. "Some may be more guilty than others but they've all got to be cleared out. Four are in town, twelve in surrounding hideaways. They have plenty of other sympathizers. Slim Sheets made that clear. If we go to town first, someone is sure to slip away and warn the others. We want to do this job so completely that there'll never have to be a Vigilante Committee again."

Two men, Wade Cook and another, were sent back to town to watch the four known outlaws living there. Jed sent Cook because he couldn't bear to watch the fellow's savage enjoyment of the hangings that would come soon.

The posse was two days making the roundup. They caught nine of the twelve men they were after and hanged them all. Just before they strung up the last one they were joined by Wade Cook.

"It's all over the country what we're doing," he proclaimed. "Half the toughs in Gold Reef are pullin' out, and if we don't hurry, we won't get to hang any of them at all."

"If they pull out, why should we want to hang them?" Jed demanded.

Cook looked at the captain as though he had suddenly come unhinged. "But they ought to be hanged. Two of the four on our list have already left town. Maybe they'll gather up a crowd of outlaws and come back. Nobody knows what might happen."

Jed's throat was unaccountably dry. "Which ones got away?" he asked.

"Jim Smith, the deputy sheriff, and Jack Marlo. Burke and Lonergan are still there, pretending to be law-abidin' men. I want to see their faces when we show 'em Slim's confession."

A sound of relief whistled through Jed's teeth. If Marlo had gotten away, surely he wouldn't be fool enough to come back.

"Let's get this job over, boys, so we can try to strike the town just after dark," he told his followers.

He found himself participating in this hanging with an almost impersonal interest. He was getting hardened to the routine, and no longer had the feeling that at any moment he might betray the inner sickness which made him feel as though his stomach were full of angleworms.

One more job and the work of the Vigilantes would be done, he told himself. After the completion of this roundup the road agents would never dare to openly flaunt their colors again. Regularly elected law officers would be able to handle any trouble that might arise.

The twenty-three men in his company rode quietly into town and turned their mounts into Hawley's corral, back of the livery barn. They divided into two companies. One group went to get a professional gambler named Charlie Lonergan; the other, led by Captain Hawley, went to the courthouse to pick up Tim Burke, Gold Reef's leading butcher.

Burke offered no resistance. "I heard you stranglers were out on a raid, but I thought you had too much sense to try your criminal activities on a prominent businessman," he blustered.

"Where is Jim Smith?" Jed asked.

"He went out to arrest you fellows," Burke retorted. "If you think for a minute the honest people of this town will stand by and see respectable citizens lynched—"

"This isn't a lynching, Burke," Jed interrupted. "You were named as the leader of the road-agent organization in Slim Sheets's confession. Two others of the men we had to hang corroborated that confession. You'll have your chance to disprove what they said, but you'll have to talk fast. You'll get no more consideration than the others."

The butcher glanced around with startled eyes. He saw no relenting in the drawn, somber faces of men who looked upon his execution as the fitting climax of their grim duties. Burke, Lonergan, and Marlo—these were the Big Three of the road agents.

Burke reacted to formula; the Vigilantes were growing weary of it. He cursed Slim Sheets bitterly, protested his innocence, blamed evil companions for his downfall, threw himself upon the ground, and begged abjectly for his life. Then he cursed his executioners, and finally pulled himself together in a pitiful attempt to die with some show of dignity.

Lonergan had been brought in. Unlike the others, he remained calm and quiet, watching Burke with a look of cynical amusement upon his too-white cheeks.

All the time Jed Hawley was wondering how Jack Marlo would have taken it if he had been here with the others. Would he have begged and cursed like Burke or faced death bravely like Lonergan? Sixteen men had faced the rope up until now, and fifteen of the sixteen had weakened. Yet Jack's professed creed was that since a man must die when his time comes, the means and manner of its coming couldn't matter. Perhaps, if he had been captured, he would have lived up to that creed.

There were certain formalities to be observed and Jed noticed, with disgust that bordered on hatred, how eager Wade Cook was to get at the hanging. It was hard for him to keep from kicking the bloodthirsty little man, just to relieve his feelings. It came to him with considerable shock that Cook, heretofore a colorless little prig of a man, had by his very vehemence and savagery grown in importance until he had constituted himself a sort of special prosecutor.

"Where's Jack Marlo?" Cook snapped suddenly. "He's the one we really want to get. He's the worst one of the lot."

"Turn us loose and maybe we'll be able to find him for you," Lonergan offered cynically.

Jed was aware of covert glances in his direction. Most of the men knew that he and his wife had been on friendly terms with the Marlos. Some of them knew that Jed and Jack were comrades of long standing.

"Get this over with," he ordered harshly.

Never had he hoped for anything so much as he now hoped the work of the Vigilantes was over. The strain had been great on all of them, and they showed it. They dispersed almost without a word.

Jed went directly to the livery stable and washed his hands

thoroughly before going home. He dreaded the look he was going to see on Jolene's face.

There was no light in the house and he discovered in a moment that Jolene was not home. He had one panicky moment before he noticed her note on the table.

"Jed, if I'm not back when you get home, I'll be down to Isabel's. Please come for me. Jolene."

The girls had heard something, he was sure. Possibly Jack Marlo had told his wife why he had to pull out. Jolene opened the door when he knocked.

"Oh, Jed!" she cried.

He kissed her, patted her hair and her shoulder. She drew him inside and gazed searchingly into his face.

"Is Jack with you?" she asked.

"Come out here," he ordered, and seized her arm. But he saw Isabel over Jolene's shoulder. "Hello, Isabel," he said uncertainly. "Will you excuse us a moment?"

"Don't go outside. I'll go in the kitchen," Isabel said. "You haven't had supper, have you? I'll start some."

"Don't bother, please."

"I'll make some coffee, anyway, Captain. You look like you need it."

"Well?" Jolene's voice was strange.

"Good God, Jolene, haven't you wised up yet? Jack has been a messenger for the road agents."

"You mean you . . . you and those murderers you've been leading have hanged him?" In her dark eyes he saw lights dancing that had never been there before.

"I never thought to have my own wife call me a murderer," he said. "But we didn't hang Jack. He ran away."

"Thank God for that. Night after night I've told Isabel that Jack was with you. We both thought he was a Vigilante. We must never let her find out."

"Some things can't be helped, Jolene. By morning everybody in Gold Reef will know what he was. She'll have to know. Lord, woman, you don't think I *wanted* to hang those men? All I hope is that Jack keeps on going."

Jed had failed to quite close the door, but in the intensity of their conversation they did not hear the footsteps coming up the path until the door was thrown open and Jack Marlo, a smile on his handsome face, stood there looking at them.

"Well! Company," he said. "Good!"

"Jack, come inside and shut the door!" Jolene screamed.

This brought Isabel from the kitchen. She darted over to her husband and threw herself into his arms. He kissed her, held her off at arm's length.

"What's going on here?" he asked quizzically. "Somebody died?"

"It's no use bluffing, Jack," Jed said. "You shouldn't have come back."

"It's my home, isn't it?"

Jolene asked in a strained voice, "Jack, it isn't true, is it, that you're a road agent?"

"Whatever gave you that idea?"

"Slim Sheets gave it to me," Jed said bluntly. "His confession named you as messenger. There are plenty of other things that link up. We hanged Burke and Lonergan less than an hour ago. Only Jim Smith and three others escaped. You made the biggest mistake of your life, Jack, when you came back here."

"I heard you stranglers were getting hard with some of the boys, but even if I'm hanged I reckon I'd still rather be me than you."

"Why did you come back?"

"Best reason in the world—because my wife is here. If I could get a fair trial I could prove I'm innocent. I suppose, though, I wouldn't stand a chance with your stranglers." Marlo's voice was getting ugly.

"God knows why you came," Captain Jed sighed. "You must have known you couldn't bluff it out."

"You mean, you—"

"Oh, no!" Jolene cried.

"That's about it, Jack," Jed said.

Marlo drew his gun and pressed it against Hawley's stomach. The two white-faced young wives gasped helplessly.

"Don't get excited, girls," Jed said calmly. "He won't shoot. Killing me wouldn't help him."

"Yes, damn you, I know it," Marlo said bitterly. "If that yellow-livered Sheets talked, I suppose the jog is up—unless you help me."

"Of course we'll help you," Jolene exclaimed.

"I'm afraid we can't now, Jack," Jed contradicted. "So many of you fellows are too proud to run until it's too late. Burke crumpled up; Lonergan took it like a man. I'll take your gun now."

It was the captain the young women were watching, not Marlo, as he took the gun and stuck it inside the waistband of his trousers. Something had happened to Marlo. He looked the same but something buoyant had gone out of him. He had ridden the stream of life high and airily. Now he was waterlogged.

"Jed Hawley," Jolene spoke slowly and distinctly, "if you turn Jack over to those—those 'stranglers,' you and I are through."

"We don't call ourselves stranglers, Jolene. We're Vigilantes. Jack, here, is just as guilty as any one of the men we've had to hang. If I said let him go, it would be the same as saying the others should have been let go. Then I would be the murderer you called me."

It was all he could say for himself, and he knew it. He wasn't a dramatic man; his voice didn't have the resonance and hypnotic fervor necessary to sway another person's emotions. Jolene had to accept his plea on simple faith and logic or not at all.

"You told me Jack saved your life once," she reminded him.

A knock at the door caught them all unawares. Jed looked past his wife at Isabel. Her round, childish face was full of bewilderment and fright.

"Open up!" came the jubilant voice of Wade Cook. "It's the Vigilantes, Marlo, and we know you're in there."

The other three persons in the room looked at Captain Hawley.

"If Jack hid in another room and you told them he wasn't

here they'd go away," Jolene said. "He could escape. You owe him that."

"No."

"Jed, I warned you," Jolene's usually soft voice sounded high and shrill and hysterical. "If you don't at least try to save Jack from that mob, I'll leave you!"

"Better come out, Marlo, because we watched you go in," Cook shouted from the outside. "Nothing you can do now will keep you from kicking air alongside Burke and Lonergan."

"You said you hated to hang men. That man doesn't sound like it," Jolene said bitterly.

Jed couldn't deny it. He'd never hated anyone so much as he hated Wade Cook. Jack Marlo, for all his crime, was worth a dozen Cooks. And all he himself had to do was walk out there and say, "You're wrong. It was me you saw coming here."

He stepped to the door and said, "Keep your mouth shut, Cook. Marlo is coming along quietly."

As he opened the door, strength and understanding began to build in him. Warmly human sorrow lingered, but there had to be in them all acceptance of the harsh needs of an untamed country.

Isabel was young and pretty. Present tragedy would pass with the love of some better man than Jack Marlo. As for Jolene, already he could see in her tragic, sorrowing eyes a reflection of the courage and the staunch, unshakable faith that was a pioneer wife's mightiest armor.

Mochila Mail—
Epoch of Courage

BY GLENN SHIRLEY

"THE Pony Express!"

A graphic phrase, painting in the mind the picture of a horse, its light, lean rider, brown and whipcord hard, bent low against the wind, galloping at full speed across the prairie, mountains, and desert to deliver the mail.

The Pony Express was one of the briefest of frontier ventures. It lasted only eighteen months.

But in that short period it wrote an immortal saga of determination and endurance of the American pioneer who opened the West.

The whole experiment was quixotic. It bankrupted the company which sponsored it and was in fact a colossal failure. Yet no other episode in the colorful annals of our westward expansion typified so completely the American spirit of free enterprise. And nothing since has so stirred the imagination of adventure-loving generations beyond reason as the courage and derring-do of its riders who, on our borders little more than a century ago, accepted the challenge of distance and danger and rode with the mighty compulsions of honor, pride, and duty to see that the mail went through.

Early writers on the Express and today's cold-trailing historians disagree on its actual founding. The latter point to Genghis Khan, conqueror of Tartary and China, as the first to conceive of a horse relay for communication during his reign from 1206 to 1227 A.D., and mention that, in a later age, enterprising editors in New York and Boston used the system to gather news and election returns in the 1820s and 1830s, until the telegraph made it obsolete. It is doubtful, however, that Senator William M. Gwin of California had heard of either.

In the fall of 1854 Senator Gwin made a trip from San Francisco to Washington, D.C., on horseback, by way of Salt Lake City and South Pass, then known as the Central Route. For a part of his journey he was accompanied by a frontier scout and former cavalry corporal named Benjamin F. Ficklin. California by this time held a large and enterprising population. Utah had become a territory in 1850. The nearly half-million United States citizens living west of the Rockies were starved for news from cities and loved ones they had left behind. The rail lines and telegraph stopped at St. Joseph on the Missouri River. The overland stage lines which had been operating over the Oregon Trail, Santa Fe Trail, and the Salt Lake route proved unsatisfactory as mail carriers, taking nearly thirty days to bridge the gap with the East. The great bulk of mail was brought by slow steamer up the coast after a long Atlantic voyage and carriage across the Isthmus of Panama on a twenty-three-day schedule from New York to San Francisco. Ficklin jokingly told the California Senator that his term might expire while he was traveling to Washington to take office, and suggested that stations set up at intervals along the Central Route, with men and horses to relay letters from station to station across the continent in both directions at the same time, could cut the communication time between East and West almost in half.

His enthusiasm was contagious. Senator Gwin was certain the plan would work, despite the soaring mountains, deep snows, mighty rivers, and fierce Indians. In January 1855 he introduced a bill providing for the establishment of a weekly letter express between St. Louis and San Francisco, the schedule to be ten days, the compensation not to exceed $5000 for the round trip, and the route to be from the Missouri to Salt Lake and over the Sierras as Ficklin suggested. The bill was referred to the Committee on Military Affairs and never heard of afterward.

During the next five years Congress concerned itself largely with matters presaging the Civil War; but the people of the West, and particularly of the Pacific Coast, continued to agitate for accelerated mail service. In 1858 John Butterfield began running his stages over the Southern Route, looping down from Missouri through Arkansas and Indian Territory to El Paso, across New Mexico, down the valley of the Gila in Arizona, and thence into southern California. The inexperienced and poorly supported Post Office Department granted a meager subsidy to his company. But Butterfield's best time from St. Louis to San Francisco was only twenty-one days, little sooner than the old steamship way, though phenomenally fast for stagecoaches covering twenty-eight hundred miles.

The Californians kept hammering at Congress. The main route hacked across the plains and mountains by these pioneers with their slow-moving wagon trains had been direct enough—why was it being ignored now? It was argued that it would be impossible to keep a more northerly route open summer and winter. The fact was the South's representatives in Congess, by their concentrated votes, were able to prevent legislation favorable to a route north of the slaveholding states, and confine government subsidies to the southern routes. California became more impatient than ever.

By 1860 the rumblings between the Northern and Southern states were loud and ominous. Now that war appeared inevitable, men of vision in the West faced the harsh question, "How will it affect *us?*" It became evident that both the Southern Stage Route and the Panama Route would be liable to interruption upon the opening of hostilities, and besides, it was of utmost importance that quicker communication be had with the Washington authorities. While Northern men were in a majority in California, the Southern sympathizers were numerous and making every effort to carry the state out of the Union.

Gwin, convinced finally that government aid for a pony service could not be obtained because of the Southern bloc, managed to interest his old friend William H. Russell, senior partner of the big pioneer freighting firm of Russell, Majors and Waddell, in undertaking the mail run through the Central Route as a private venture.

Russell was born January 31, 1812, in Burlington, Vermont.

He had migrated to Missouri at a time when that territory was the outpost of Western expansion. He began work at sixteen as a clerk, later becoming a merchant and a partner in a bank at Richmond, and by the late 1840s was engaged in freighting on government contracts.

Alexander Majors was born near Franklin, in Simpson County, Kentucky, October 4, 1814. When he was three, his family moved to Missouri, where they acquired an extensive farm, with saw and flour mills in Jackson County. Alexander worked on the farm and as a miller's boy, until he married in 1834 and began farming on his own. In August 1848 he began carrying freight from Independence to Santa Fe with an outfit of six wagons and teams. Majors was a man with a keen, practical business sense. His first trip, completed in ninety-two days, netted him $1500. Also a man of deep religious convictions, he became the oddest boss freighter ever to ply the Western trails. He refused to work on Sunday, and made his employees pledge not to cuss, drink, gamble, treat animals cruelly, "or do anything else incompatible with the conduct of a gentleman." He paid good wages, else he would have had difficulty hiring a crew. In December 1854 he joined Russell and W. B. Waddell in a freighting partnership with headquarters at Leavenworth, Kansas. The company hired more than four thousand men, owned forty thousand oxen and a thousand mules, and operated 6250 wagons west of St. Joseph. Shipments traveled in trains of twenty-five wagons each, with stations several miles apart, as far west as Salt Lake City.

Majors took full responsibility for all business on the roads. Under his shrewd management the firm grew rapidly. In 1855-56, the profits of their ambitious venture topped $300,000. In 1857, a contract was obtained for supplying the Army ordered to Utah. The firm expanded. In May 1859, Russell and a John S. Jones opened a stage line from Leavenworth to Denver, which was taken over by the firm the next year. In February 1860 the Central Overland and Pike's Peak Express company was chartered with Russell as president, running first-class coaches through to California.

Little is known of Waddell, the third partner, except that he had been taken into the firm because of his money and ability to get financial backing. Russell spent most of his time lobbying in Washington for government contracts. It was during one of these periods that Gwin convinced him of the feasibility of a through pony mail to San Francisco. The success of the enterprise, together with the probable closing of the present mail routes and the necessity of finding some other not liable to interference from the South, also held forth the possibility of wresting the $125,000 mail concession to California from their strongest competitor, John Butterfield.

Majors and Waddell strongly objected to the wildly imaginative scheme. They could not see even expenses in the undertaking. But Russell insisted that the project would eventually lead to a paying proposition. Besides, he already had given the Senator and his friends his word.

This settled the matter. The word of the firm, once given by one of its members, was to them as binding as a written obligation. They unitedly threw their whole energy and resources into carrying out the pledge, and thus rushed into existence what became known as the Pony Express.

They associated with themselves as incorporators of the new company John S. Jones and William W. Finney, employees of the firm, and Ben Ficklin, then general superintendent of their Western division. Ficklin had joined Russell, Majors, and Waddell when their wagon trains were hauling millions of pounds of supplies to General Albert Sidney Johnston over the Great Salt Lake Trail, as he marched west in the Mormon war, and was with them when the severe winter froze their teams and came near destroying the Army before it straggled into Fort Bridger, Wyoming Territory. When Russell and Jones opened the stage line to Colorado and organized the Central Overland and Pike's Peak Express, Ficklin had bought several hundred Kentucky mules and fifty Concord coaches, laid out the route, and started them rolling. He now helped the firm acquire the mail contract and stage outfit of George Chorpenning, who operated a monthly service between Salt Lake and Sacramento and, antedating the Pony by a little less than two years, had established a one-time horseback run along a route south of the Humboldt River. Finney was placed in charge at San Francisco. Ficklin was sent to Salt Lake City to make the necessary arrangements there. Arrangements in the East were left to Russell.

At Salt Lake City, Ficklin sat down with J. C. Brumley, resident agent for the company, to figure a schedule, designate relay points, and compute the required number of men and horses. They came up with something like sixty riders, 420 horses, and a hundred additional stationkeepers. The firm already had stations along its established route from St. Joseph to Salt Lake at about twenty-five mile intervals. But to expect a horse to run at top speed this distance was not logical. More stations had to be spotted an average of ten miles apart—a little less or longer, depending on the terrain. A number of old fur-trading posts and trapper and buffalo-hunter cabins were easily converted as the trail dipped west from Missouri to Marysville, Kansas, swung northwest to Rock Creek, Nebraska, to Fort Kearny, thence along the North Platte to Julesburg in the northeast corner of Colorado, looped north past Fort Laramie to Independence Rock in Wyoming, up the treacherous defiles of South Pass and down to Fort Bridger.

Salt Lake was next, and the largest settlement after leaving St. Joseph. The land west of Salt Lake City, particularly beyond Ruby Valley, was almost total emptiness. There was rarely a convenient ranch or settlement. Chorpenning, in his heyday, had spotted no more than fourteen stations along his line, and additional ones had to be built by crews sent out from Utah and California. Also some changes in the route were necessary as it swung to Fort Churchill and Carson City, Nevada, west over Carson Pass into California through the unpredictable snowy Sierras to Placerville, and then over friendlier terrain to Sacramento.

The horses were selected with great care. They definitely were "horses" rather than "ponies." Three hundred purchased in Salt Lake and from the Army quartermaster at Fort Leavenworth were "from four to seven years old, not exceeding fifteen hands high, warranted sound, and suitable for running." A hundred and twenty-nine more obtained in San Francisco were "native California stock." Many were hammerheaded, half-wild mustangs. A few were crossed with thoroughbred racing strains. All were rangy, long-legged, and tough. It was their speed and intestinal fortitude that counted. The rigorous schedule called for virtually two hundred miles of distance to be covered every twenty-four hours the breadth of the nearly two thousand miles to be traversed twice as fast as stagecoach travel in early 1860.

Each horse traveled his allotted span like a shot from a gun. Nothing swerved him from his path. Neither trackless prairies nor swollen streams nor desert sands. Narrow cliffside trails were taken in stride. Not even the rugged, snowswept Sierras could halt the horses of the Pony Express. They were picked for one purpose—race the mail from their starting point to the next relay station, and on the return trip, race it back again. They were always kept in the best condition to make them long-lasting enough to outrun the swift ponies of the Plains Indians.

Most of these gallant, salty animals scattered along the 154 relay stations were never more than half-broken throughout their career in the service. Many never quit lunging, bucking, and sunfishing every time a rider swung aboard.

Obviously horses were at a greater premium than handlers and riders, because they were already in corrals at both ends of the line before this first tiny advertisement appeared in the Sacramento *Union,* of March 19:

MEN WANTED! The undersigned wishes to hire ten or a dozen men, familiar with the management of horses, as hostlers, or riders on the Overland Express Route via Salt Lake City. Wages $50 per month and found. I may be found at the St. George Hotel during Sunday, Monday and Tuesday.

WILLIAM W. FINNEY

The response was instantaneous. On the afternoon of the second day the *Union* announced that "the requisite number of postriders on the Overland Express had been engaged." Similar results were achieved at the eastern terminal in St. Joseph.

Rider applicants had to meet a fairly standardized set of qualifications, supposedly set up by Alexander Majors, who was personally familiar with the hazards of the route and the daily strain a man must endure. All had to be between eighteen and twenty years of age, maximum weight 125 pounds, wiry, sound of mind and limb, and of course accomplished, fearless horsemen—a requirement easy to come by in this broad, uncharted land of mountain and prairie loneliness and bloodied death, where boys grew to manhood early and virtually in the saddle. There was little question as to their motives. Certainly the risk was worth more than the "$50 a month and found" offered. Any lad could have earned twice the amount on river boats and levees along the Pacific Coast and Missouri River, or in the fabulous Washoe Mines by scaling the Sierras. It was the excitement, the challenge and infinity of proud glory, that attracted them. Some told their age with slight exaggeration to become eligible.

Each was given a small Bible and required to take the following oath: "I . . . do hereby swear, before the Great and Living God, that during my engagement with Russell, Majors and Waddell I will under no circumstances use profane language; that I will drink no intoxicating liquors; that I will not quarrel or fight with any other employee of the firm, and that in every respect, I will conduct myself honestly, be faithful to my duties, and so direct all my acts as to win the confidence of my employers. And I agree, if I violate any of the above conditions, to accept my discharge without any pay for my services. So help me, God."

Whether it was the oath, the Bible, or the fear of losing their wages, the riders responded with such almost evangelistic fervor that Majors wrote, in his later years: "I do not remember a single instance of a man signing these rules being discharged without pay."

No effort was made to uniform them. They dressed as their individual fancy dictated, but as conservatively as possible. The usual costume consisted of a buckskin hunting shirt, cloth trousers tucked into a pair of high boots, jingling spurs, and a jockey cap or slouch hat with a flattened front brim as a brace against the wind.

All rode armed, but seldom with more than a sheath knife or revolver. Some carried a Navy Colt of the 1851 model, then a popular weapon. Due to its ponderous weight—it was a huge, five-shot, percussion-fired, .36-caliber pistol with an octagonal-shaped barrel—it was never in general use, however. Most riders preferred the Wells Fargo-model Colt. A short pocket pistol with a three-inch, octagonal-shaped barrel, it was percussion-fired and five-shot like the Navy, but used a lighter, .31-caliber ball. Although not so powerful a weapon, it served the purpose just as well, speed being the riders' chief protection against desperadoes and hostile Indians.

The horse's accouterments also stressed the lightness of the load carried. A hybrid of the Western and jockey-type saddle was designed and built by historic saddleries in St. Louis, San Francisco, and Sacramento. It was made on the California tree handed down from the *vaqueros,* with a center-fire rigging, a short, broad horn and low, sloping cantle, the merest skeleton of skirts and other leather covering, and light wooden stirrups with *tapaderas* to fend off the brush. The finished product weighed only a third as much as the regular stock saddle then in use on the frontier. Its over-all length was about forty inches, but it was roomy enough to afford the necessary comfort for riding long distances at top speed.

Without the least distracting from the courage of the riders selected, the Express managers realized the horses were nevertheless the real heroes of the service, and the mail was fastened directly to the horse, rather than the rider. An unhorsed rider was helpless to get the mail through on time, or at all. But horses could, and did, time and again come thundering into their relay points as fast as their flying hoofs could carry them, the mail secure on empty saddles.

Accordingly, over this entire equine seat was thrown the storied *mochila,* or leather covering, with slits through which projected the horn and cantle. Attached to its broad skirt, two on either side, one in front and behind each thigh of the rider when mounted, were four *cantinas,* or hard leather boxes, to carry the mail. Ordinary mail pouches or saddlebags—contrary to shoot-

'em-up motion pictures and fiction written about the subject—
were too bulky to handle and would have caused undue delay
in changing mounts. The *cantinas* were secured with brass locks.
Three of these were opened en route at military posts and at
Salt Lake City, and under no circumstances at any other place.
The fourth was for way stations, where each keeper had a key,
and contained a waybill, or timecard, on which a record of
arrival and departure was kept.

The same *mochila* was transferred from pony to pony and
from rider to rider until it reached one terminus or the other. At
ten- to fifteen-mile intervals the rider would dismount on the run,
strip off the *mochila* in one easy motion, toss it over the horn
and cantle of the saddle already cinched on a fresh horse, and
take off again in a matter of seconds.

The combined weight of the saddle, *mochila,* and *cantinas*
never exceeded fourteen pounds. The mail itself was limited to
twenty pounds, but usually totaled about fifteen. The thinnest
paper obtainable was used for letters, which were rolled to pencil
size and carefully wrapped with oilskin before insertion in the
compartments. This protected the mail when a rider was caught
in torrential storms or had to cross swollen streams. Special
editions of Eastern newspapers were printed on tissue paper in
order for them to reach subscribers on the Pacific Coast. This was
mostly for advertisement, since there was little demand for them
at their necessarily high price. The charges were five dollars for
each letter of one-half ounce or less, in addition to the regular
United States postage.

Within sixty days the operating sections of the line had been
organized and the Pony put under saddle. Meanwhile Russell
had made arrangements in major cities of the East to accumu-
late mail for forwarding to the eastern terminus of the Express
at St. Joseph. His own New York office was designated as the
agency there. Other offices were established in Washington,
D.C., Chicago, and St. Louis. At any of these both businessmen
and private individuals could deposit mail for California and
way points.

On March 26, 1860, the following advertisement appeared in the New York *Herald*, the St. Louis *Republican,* and other papers:

To San Francisco in 8 days by the C.O.C. & P.P. Ex. Co. The first courier of the Pony Express will leave the Missouri River on Tuesday, April 3rd, at 5 P.M., and will run regularly weekly hereafter, carrying a letter mail only. The point on the Mo. River will be in telegraphic connection with the east and will be announced in due time.

Telegraphic messages from all parts of the United States and Canada in connection with the point of departure will be received up to 5:00 P.M. of the day of leaving and transmitted over the Placerville & St. Jo to San Francisco and intermediate points by the connecting express in 8 days. The letter mail will be delivered in San Francisco in 10 days from the departure of the express. The express passes through Forts Kearny, Laramie, Bridger, Great Salt Lake City, Camp Floyd, Carson City, The Washoe Silver Mines, Placerville and Sacramento, and letters for Oregon, Washington Territory, British Columbia, the Pacific Mexican ports, Russian possessions, Sandwich Islands, China, Japan and India will be mailed in San Francisco.

Special messengers, bearers of letters to connect with the express of the 3rd of April, will receive communications for the courier of that day at 481 10th St., Washington City, up to 2:45 P.M. of Friday, March 30th, and in New York at the office of J. B. Simpson, Room No. 8 Continental Bank Building, Nassau St., up to 6:50 P.M. of 31st March.

Full particulars can be obtained on application at the above places and from the agents of the company.

On April 3 everything was ready. The nation was thrilled. Despite grave doubts from some quarters that the venture was "simply inviting slaughter upon all the foolhardy young men who have been engaged as riders," the entire populace of St. Jo gathered on the banks of the Missouri to see the first doughty Expressman leap astride his impatient steed and dash away through a curtain of legend.

For more than half a century the town had served as a transportation center and gateway to the West. It had been named for the patron saint of Joseph Robidoux, who as early as 1803 had traded with the Indians at Blacksnake Hills. The name had been changed from Robidoux's Trading Post to St. Joseph in 1843. The launching of the Express was another great event in the city's glorious and exciting history.

Russell and Alexander Majors were present with Mayor M. Jeff Thompson to lend the affair a "proper sense of dignity and aplomb." From 5 P.M.—the time of departure promised by Russell in his advertising—until after dark, solemn speeches were delivered. Curiously, the rider was delayed two hours and fifteen minutes. Russell was not disheartened. He did not speak, but both Majors and Mayor Thompson were verbose in declaring the Pony "the harbinger of the Pacific railroad," while the crowd waited for the arrival of the mail from the east.

A special train consisting of a wood-burner engine, *The Missouri,* with tender and one car had been sent 160 miles east to Hannibal to meet a special messenger carrying the Pony Express mail from the big city off-line agencies. The messenger missed his connection at Detroit. Word was flashed to George H. Davis, the roadmaster at Hannibal. Davis immediately ordered all trains off the main line and every switch spiked. Addison Clark, a "nervy, fearless engineer," took the throttle. Fuel agents between Hannibal and St. Joseph were instructed to stand by to reload the tender, and Clark was told to "make a speed record that will last fifty years!"

When the messenger climbed aboard at Hannibal, Addison Clark took off in "a cloud of steam and smoke." He covered the first seventy miles of narrow, unseasoned roadbed at sixty miles per hour; then through Macon City to the fuel stop at Coleman, where men with armloads of wood were waiting on the platform. Within seconds the tender was replenished and the train sped crazily away again. Clark took the steep grade down the Chariton River "like an avalanche," hot fire blasting from the stack and "wood sparks streaming backwards like crimson snowflakes." No other engineer ever equaled his time over that section of railroad. He reached St. Joseph at 7:15 P.M., having covered the dangerous 206-mile run at an average speed of fifty miles per hour.

When Clark "stepped majestically from his iron horse, looking mussed up, grimy and grand," he was the hero of the moment, the Pony Express almost forgotten. No one even learned the messenger's name. He simply turned the mail pouch over to station officials and vanished—forever. The pouch contained forty-nine letters, five telegrams, and several newspapers—a payload of about $800. The contents were transferred to a waiting *mochila* by Joseph S. Roberson, a station employee. Russell himself threw the *mochila* over the saddle of the waiting pony. Then the rider mounted.

No one has been able to determine, with complete accuracy, the name of the rider. He has been variously identified as Alex Carlisle, William Richardson, Gus Cliff, Henry Wallace, and Johnny Frey; Frey is the one most often mentioned.

Whoever the rider was, he wore a bright red shirt, blue trousers stuffed into gay flower-worked leggings, and plated jingling spurs, "resembling for all the world a fantastic circus performer." His horse, a big sorrel said to be named Sylph, was equipped with harness bearing sparkling silver mountings.

The crowd cheered madly. Russell and Majors shook hands with each other and Mayor Thompson. Then came the booming roar of a cannon. . . . Little Johnny Frey dug his spurs into the sorrel's flanks and the powerful animal leaped forward in a dead run. The furious pace lasted only a few blocks to Jules Street, where the ferry *Denver* waited to carry Frey, his pony and cargo to Elwood across the Missouri. Earlier in the day Frey had left his work garments on the ferry. The public's fancy had been humored by his festive adornment, and he shifted now to his tough trail clothes. Only a fool would give an Indian or desperado a red shirt and flashing accouterments for a target while crossing the plains. At 7:30 P.M., or shortly thereafter, he spurred up the slippery bank on the Kansas shore, and galloped off into the afterglow of the sunset.

According to the most reliable reports, he rode to Granada, where Don Rising took over. Rising gave the *mochila* to Jack Keetley at Maryville. Keetley carried it to Hollenberg. The next major station was Fort Kearny, but there is no clear record as to the men who carried the first Pony mail beyond Hollenberg.

It isn't important anyway. What is important was that at the same moment, two thousand miles away in San Francisco, a man named James Randall mounted "a clean-limbed hardy little nankeen-colored pony" tethered at the door of the Alta Telegraph Company's office on Montgomery Street. In Randall's *mochila* were fifty-six letters, a payload of $280 at five dollars per half ounce. Bands played, flags waved, and another great crowd cheered wildly as he sent the horse flying down to the waterfront and the river steamer *Antelope,* which would take him to Sacramento. The *Antelope* tied up to the Sacramento levee at 2:40 the next morning. Thirteen letters from Sacramento writers —such an embarrassing quantity that the local newspaper didn't mention it for a week—were added to the cargo. Then Randall handed the *mochila* to Sam Hamilton, the first lad to begin the long ride to the east.

With no more than a wave and "Good luck!" from the telegraph agent, the early hour being no inducement for a gay celebration, Hamilton took the White Rock road, stopping at Five Mile House, Fifteen Mile House, Mormon Tavern, Mud Springs, and Diamond Springs to change horses. At 6:40 A.M., he was in Placerville. A few minutes later, on another fresh horse, he was on his way up the mountains. An hour and twelve miles farther, he reached Sportsman's Hall, where he passed the *mochila* to the second rider, Warren Upson.

Upson is worth more than a passing mention. The son of a prominent California family, barely out of his teens, he possessed a superb physique, was an excellent horseman, and knew the mountain country better than the Latin verbs he had learned from an overdose of formal education to which he had rebelled. He continued eastward at full gallop in a spitting snowstorm that had blown up. He knew what might be ahead, and had selected a station pony for sturdiness rather than speed. The situation was worse than expected.

The storm turned into a white nightmare and brought the busy traffic to the Washoe Mines to a standstill. By the time Upson reached the summit, his horse was floundering through huge drifts and the trail and landmarks were blotted out in the swirling blizzard. The cold was intense. But he fought doggedly on. He found fresh horses at the established relay points and managed to reach Hope Valley. The stationkeeper warned:

"Upson, you're a fool!"

The determined youngster flung back: "Nothing must stop the Pony Express!"

He pushed on to Woodford's and took the sharp decline down

to Genoa. A last change of mounts here, and he was on the last leg of his run to Carson City. Upson arrived at the little Nevada community of twelve hundred only a few minutes behind schedule, having covered nearly ninety miles of snow-buried, murderously narrow trails over the Sierra Nevadas.

Again the record is unclear as to the name of the rider who rushed the mail from Carson City to Fort Churchill. It is almost a certainty that the famed Robert "Pony Bob" Haslam picked it up at Fort Churchill and carried on through Pah-Ute country to Smith's Creek. H. J. Faust, later a prominent physician in Utah, seems to have been the rider from Jacob Station to Ruby Valley; Josh Perkins from Ruby to Shell Creek; Jim Gentry from Shell Creek to Deep Creek; Let Huntington to Simpson's Springs; and John Fisher to Camp Floyd, where Howard Egan took over, bringing the *mochila* into Salt Lake City at 11:45 P.M., April 7.

A storm east of Salt Lake slowed the Pony's progress and it took the next rider five hours to cover the twenty-five miles to Snyder's Mill. From here, road conditions gradually improved. Station after station, agonizing mile after mile, the mail moved unceasingly eastward to Fort Bridger, Horseshoe, Gilman's Ranch, always onward, to Fort Kearny, Liberty Farm, Hollenberg. At last, little Johnny Frey picked it up at Granada. At 3:55 P.M. on April 13, Frey boarded the ferry at Elwood, Kansas, and crossed the Missouri to St. Joseph. A noisy throng greeted him with loud cheers, bonfires, and the clanging of church bells. At the Patee House, where the company had its office, the cannon again boomed a salute, and the local militia, in full uniform, paraded the streets and fired their rifles. Wires reached New York the same afternoon. For the first time in American history communications between East and West had been achieved in ten days!

Meanwhile the westbound Express had passed the eastbound Pony near Salt Lake City, raced on through the Utah Territory, and reached Carson City at 3:30 P.M., April 12. Here the amazing Warren Upson picked up the mail and made another frightening crossing of the Sierras. Sam Hamilton received the *mochila* at

Sportsman's Hall, and at 5:25 on the afternoon of April 13, dashed into Sacramento and a roaring reception.

The whole city turned out to greet him with bands, bells, and guns. Making only a brief stop to deliver the mail for that point, Hamilton hurried aboard the swift steamer *Antelope* and headed downstream to the city by the Golden Gate.

News of his coming already had been flashed over the Alta telegraph, and hundreds of San Franciscans organized for the event. At 11 P.M., the California Band began "a musical migration" through the city, attracting additions until the assemblage swelled to nearly two thousand. Bonfires blazed in the streets, their flames so lurid against the midnight sky that the fire companies were summoned. Finding no fire, they, too, joined the procession. Then the huge crowd headed down to the Broadway wharf, where, during a half-hour wait, the California Band "kept enthusiasm at a peak by offering selections of martial airs and waltzes." At 12:38 A.M., the *Antelope* tied up at the dock. The procession formed into a march and escorted the rider on his bay horse to the telegraph office with rousing cheers and "a spirit that carried on until the wee small hours in various boisterous styles and harmless ways."

The seemingly impossible had been accomplished in both directions. Newspapers carried the story to every city in the East. "The Pony has galloped halfway across the continent in nine days and twenty-one hours. An amazing marvel . . . one of the gigantic enterprises of our day," it said.

The public read it with breathless interest, but President Buchanan, never one to support internal improvements by the national government, showed no indication of sharing their enthusiasm. Senator Gwin orated loud and long, but Congress, too concerned with the great discussion of slavery and the national situation, paid no attention to him.

History had been made. But a different sort of story was to be written in the coming year and a half—a story of incredible bravery and hardship, of death and injury, of Indian fighting and outlaw raids, along the route of the Pony Express.

At first, things worked smoothly. Located every two hundred

miles were division agents to exercise general supervision over the service and provide for emergencies when a station was sacked and robbed and its stock stampeded. Considering the isolation of relay posts, the loss of stock and personnel was extraordinarily small as the result of usual dangers of the frontier.

Most of the employees who lost their lives in the service were killed by Indians during the months of May and June of 1860, when the Pah-Utes and their northern brethren, the Shoshonis and Bannocks, went on the warpath in Nevada and Utah. The entire route from Salt Lake to Carson City was affected. Nearly all the stations between the two points were burned or otherwise destroyed, the horses stolen, and the keepers either murdered or driven from the country. The service was suspended for several weeks. The whole enterprise might have been abandoned but for the energetic efforts of an agent of the company, who, with the aid of the newspapers and backed by public sentiment, raised a body of volunteers, put down the outbreak, and restored the line to its original operation.

According to records available, only one rider was killed by Indians. A horse galloped into a station in Nevada with the rider slumped over the saddle horn, his lifeless body pierced by arrows. So tight was the clutch of his hand that the horse's mane had to be cut from his grasp.

It was during this period that Pony Bob Haslam made his most famous ride. Pony Bob received the eastbound May 10 mail from San Francisco at Friday's Station, south of Lake Bigler (now Tahoe), and headed for Buckland's Station, seventy-five miles away. At Reed's Station, east of Carson City, he found that the citizens' army had commandeered all relay mounts to pursue the Pah-Ute chief, Old Winnemucca. Pony Bob stopped only long enough to feed his horse, then spurred on to Buckland's. Here word had been received of the raid on Williams Station and the slaughter of its keeper and his assistants, and Haslam's relief rider refused to take the mail. Pony Bob volunteered to carry on. He changed horses at Sand Springs, thirty-five miles eastward, changed again at Cold Springs, thirty-four miles farther, and continued thirty miles to Smith's Creek, where he was finally relieved by Jay Kelley, having raced 190 miles without rest.

Nine hours later, he started his return trip with the westbound mail. At Cold Springs, he found that the place had been raided, the mount he had left there and all the other stock stolen, and the keeper was dead. He pushed on to Sand Springs, where he persuaded the keeper, Montgomery Maze, to leave the place and accompany him as far as the Sink of the Carson. Here Maze found safety with fifteen well-armed men who were on their way home from the chase after Winnemucca. Pony Bob galloped on alone. At Buckland's he swapped horses and continued his regular run across Carson Valley and up the mountain to Friday's Station. In all, he had ridden 380 miles, and the mail was only a few hours behind schedule.

Later, on another run, Pony Bob was attacked by Indians, but he reached his relief station after a remarkable ride of 120 miles in eight hours, his jaw shattered by a flint-head arrow and his left arm badly wounded.

The Express rider's remarkable resistance to fatigue was again demonstrated by Jack Keetley, a lad of nineteen, who rode the division between St. Joseph and Fort Kearny, some say, in payment of a bet. Keetley jumped on his horse at Big Sandy Station in Nebraska Territory, carried the *mochila* all the way to Elwood on the Missouri, then took the westbound mail back as far as Seneca, Kansas. His continuous ride took thirty-one hours, and the distance covered is alleged to have been 340 miles.

The greatest feat, in length of ride, has been credited to William F. Cody, the flamboyant "Buffalo Bill." By his own account, he was first hired as a mounted messenger between the wagon trains of Russell, Majors and Waddell when he was fifteen. In the spring of 1860, he became a Pony rider on a forty-five-mile run west of Julesburg, and the following year, was reassigned to the notorious Captain Jack Slade's division, on a run between Red Buttes on the North Platte and Three Crossings on the Sweetwater River, Nebraska, a distance of 116 miles.

At Three Crossings one day he found that his relief rider had been killed in a brawl the night before. There being no other rider available, Cody rode the dead man's seventy-six-mile trek to Rocky Ridge, where he met the mail going the other way and was forced to carry it back immediately over the long trail he had just covered.

According to Cody, "It was a very bad and dangerous country, but the emergency was great. . . . I pushed on with the usual rapidity, entering every relay station on time, and accomplished the round trip . . . back to Red Buttes, without a single mishap, on time," for a total of 384 miles.

Similar stories of daring and stamina of the Pony rider are legion in today's literature. Their horses, too, performed just as heroically, often traveling fifty or more miles when the rider would arrive at a change of station to find all the mounts stolen. Some ran until they dropped dead of exhaustion. Due to the nature of the business, the customary companionship that was so prevalent in the West between a man and his horse was entirely foreign to the Expressman and his mount. Their mad station-to-station dash allowed little time or inclination for a mutual acquaintance, and the rider always handled a number of different mounts. The riders, however, appreciated good horses and did not abuse them.

There is a record of one of these animals that bucked its rider off at the start of its run, plunged into and swam a swollen stream, then tore through a crowd that had gathered on the far bank to stop it, and sped away across the prairie. Later, foam-flecked and alone, it galloped into the next relay station, its regular destination—on schedule and with the mail intact.

Writers seized up these riders and their horses and made them king-sized. Their real exploits have been so embellished with legend and drama with each telling and retelling that the truth has been destroyed almost completely.

The great feat of the Pony Express was the delivery of President Lincoln's Inaugural Address in March 1861. The flying horsemen had brought to Utah, Nevada, and California the first word of his election, and President Buchanan's farewell message had been relayed from St. Joseph to Sacramento in the amazing time of seven days and nineteen hours. But great interest in Lincoln's address was felt all over the land, foreshadowing as it did the administration's policy in the coming rebellion. The news-starved West was impatient to see if civil war would actually erupt. The East, in turn, was concerned about the attitude of the West. So the company determined to break these previous records.

To this end, all horses were led out from the different stations along the route in order to reduce the distance each would have to run. Each horse averaged only ten miles, and this at its very best speed. Every precaution was taken to prevent delay, and the result stands without parallel in history: seven days and seventeen hours, an average of ten and seven-tenths miles per hour, for dispatch by means of men and horses halfway across the continent.

Afterward, the service was to carry the shocking news of the fall of Fort Sumter and the President's call for volunteers at the start of the Civil War. The California Column was organized less than an hour after word reached Sacramento.

The war was in full progress and the Express riders were covering the two thousand miles in less than eight days, but their *mochilas* didn't carry many letters. Apparently five dollars was too much for ordinary correspondence. Finally, the price was reduced to two and a half dollars a half ounce. Still the mail failed to increase. Russell, Majors and Waddell were losing thousands of dollars every month.

Russell tried to get money from Eastern bankers and was turned down. In Washington, D.C., Senator Gwin fought to see that the mail contract for California was given to him. Russell knew his chances were slim, but he clung to his one hope.

The War Department was sympathetic. Official and business correspondence was sent via the Pony Express. To it may be attributed the information that enabled the North to forestall plans of the Southern faction to carry California out of the Union. The English government also became one of the principal patrons of the service. Reports of operations of the English squadron in Chinese waters were forwarded by this route at a cost of $135 per report.

Senator Gwin was unable to obtain the mail contract for his friend, but just before Congress adjourned, he introduced a bill authorizing a subsidy in the sum of $2000 to be paid the Express for weekly service, or $3000 per month for semiweekly service, plus the right to pre-empt quarter sections of land for each twenty miles of the route. This proposal also failed, and Russell haughtily asserted that the Pony would continue to run with or without government aid.

The expenses of the line for the first sixteen months it operated were approximately:

Equipping the line	$100,000
Maintenance, $30,000 per month	480,000
Nevada Indian War	75,000
Miscellaneous	45,000
Total	$700,000

Although receipts did reach as high as $1000 per trip, in all they did not exceed $500,000, leaving a net loss of $200,000.

Owing to these heavy losses, not only in the operation of the service, but due to the depreciation of currency and the inability to make collections from the government because Congress had failed to make necessary appropriations, the company became faced with a debt of $1,800,000.

Without a mail subsidy or contract, the business was doomed. But it was the singing wire of the overland telegraph that brought an end to the Pony Express.

Congress, while failing to give Russell his mail contract, had done better by the electrical telegraph, underwriting a concession for a line from the Missouri River to California. Companies were chartered on the Pacific Coast and in Nebraska, each working from both ends toward the middle. Poles were set at the rate of five miles a day, and Pony riders, stopping for messages to add to their *mochilas,* found the advancing telegraph stations rapidly shrinking the distance they carried the mail. On

October 18, 1861, the Nebraska company opened its line from Omaha to Salt Lake City. Six days later, on October 24, the Pacific end of the line was tied in, and the gap bridged.

The Pony Express was finished. On October 25 a small advertisement appeared in the press, advising the public that the equine mail was no more.

But the Pony Express had revolutionized mail service, united East and West in the young nation with relatively rapid cross-country travel of news, and demonstrated the usefulness of the Central Route, laying the groundwork for the path of the first transcontinental railroad. Confronted with an almost impossible job to do, it did it and did it well, to the everlasting glory of man and beast. A glory incidentally that will never dim, neither in time nor in the retelling.

A Place
for Danny Thorpe

BY RAY HOGAN

H E came from the blue-shadowed mountain and deep-valleyed country of New Mexico; from the long, glittering flats of Arizona, from Texas, from Kansas—from everywhere almost and had yet to find his place in the scheme of things. In San Francisco he thought the search had ended but again failure, in the shape of Nate Tobin—Nugget Nate Tobin, the gambling king—had overtaken him. Now he was on the run, fearing for his life.

In the black shadows of Montgomery Street, he flattened himself against the clammy wall of a building and peered into the misty darkness. Newton and Stanger, two of Tobin's plug-uglies, were out there somewhere, silent, vengeful shadows still dogging his steps, still thirsting for his blood. Scarcely breathing, he waited, listened. Off in the direction of the bay a ship hooted, a lost, lonely sound in the fogbound night.

In the beginning Danny Thorpe had dreamed of being a rancher. Since he was Texas born and raised, it was a natural desire but in that broad land of tall and powerful men it soon became apparent to him that he was a misfit, a boy-man no one ever took seriously.

Eventually it set him to drifting and he moved from one territory and state to another, astray in a heedless world where his diminutive stature was continually a handicap that denied him the opportunities for which he so eagerly hungered.

Finally San Francisco, where he had heard jockeys were in demand and there was good money to be made at the race tracks . . . It had started well. He had a way with horses that brought out the best in them. In a few weeks he was recognized as one of the peers—and then Nate Tobin had stepped in. He ordered Danny to lose a certain race, voiced dire threats if he did not. Danny played it straight and his mount won easily. Tobin dropped a small fortune and quickly sent Pete Newton and Bill Stanger, two of his prize killers, to make an example of the little man who dared defy him. Danny Thorpe fled, aware of his great danger, aware, too, of another failure. He was . . .

"Got to be right along here somewheres."

Stanger's low voice cut through the muffled night. Danny drew closer to the wall, his nerves taut, heart racing. They were moving in and there was nothing he could do but wait—and hope. He had no weapon of any kind with which to defend himself, not even a pocketknife. The pistol he had once owned had been sold long ago when cash ran low.

"Ain't so sure," Newton's reply was couched in doubt. "Could've turned the other way. Sure ain't seeing no signs of him."

"He's here," Stanger said stubbornly. "Just stand quiet for a spell and listen."

Guarding his breath, Danny rode out the dragging moments. The ship in the harbor hooted again and somewhere a horse trotted over cobblestone pavement, the hoofbeats faint and hollow sounding. Saliva gathered in his mouth and he swallowed hard. Despite the coolness of the night sweat lay thick on his brow and he fought the urge to wipe it off.

A wave of frustration and anger surged through him. Why did such things always have to happen to him? Why could he never find a decent job, live an ordinary life as did other men? Why did something always happen to upset things just as he was getting set? He was finished in San Francisco, and in horse racing, thanks to Nate Tobin, whose tentacles reached far to touch and encircle the sport. He would have to move on, look for a different way to live. But what—and where?

He groaned silently at the prospect; he had tried about everything. There was little, if anything, left. And then, suddenly,

he recalled a newspaper advertisement he had read. At the time
he had thought little of it; now he brought it back to mind:

WANTED

Young, skinny, wiry fellows. Not over 18. Must be expert riders willing to risk
death daily. Orphans preferred. Wages $25 per week. Apply Central Overland
Express.

The Pony Express! It had begun operation just that spring,
carrying mail between Sacramento and St. Joseph, Missouri.
Maybe he could get on with them. His spirits lifted as this ray
of hope broke through his despair. There was a company office
in San Francisco but that, of course, was out; he could not risk
being spotted by Tobin's thugs. The division point was Sacramento, he had heard. He could go there, apply for a job.
Sacramento was a good ninety miles away, but there were always
freight wagons on the road and if a man worked it right he
could always hitch a ride.

He could do all that, he thought grimly, if he could stay
alive—could give Stanger and Newton the slip. Desperately he
began to search his mind for an idea, for some means of escape.
There must be a way—there had to be.

"I'm telling you, he ain't here," Newton's words came un-
expectedly from the darkness a dozen paces to his right. "He
headed the other way. I'm betting on it."

"You're betting on it," Stanger said mockingly. "Man needs
a reason to bet—"

"Heard a noise over there a bit ago. Could've been him."

"Could've been you dreaming."

"Naw. Reckon I know what I heard."

A small tremor raced up Danny Thorpe's spine as an idea
lodged in his mind. Pete Newton thought he had detected a
sound down the street in the opposite direction; perhaps, if he
made it definite, proved him right . . . Danny reached for his
hat, moving his arm carefully to avoid the rustle of cloth. He
took the small-brimmed headpiece in his hand, raised it high,
and sent it sailing off into the night. It struck against some
obstacle, set up a soft disturbance.

"There!" Newton said instantly. "You hear that?"

"I did," Stanger admitted grudgingly. "Come on. Let's have a look."

Danny listened to the soft scraping of the men's boots as they turned, walked toward the source of the sound. Waiting no longer, he wheeled and resisting the urge to run, he moved carefully and quietly to the far corner of the block. Once there, he gave in to the need to hurry. With luck he would find a freighter rolling north before he reached the edge of town.

Four weeks later, astride a horse lent him by bitter-tongued old Pat McCoskey, Express-line superintendent at Sacramento, he was on the way to Smith's Crossing, in mid-Nevada. In his pocket was his assignment to the post which would be his home station; behind him lay seventeen days of intensive training in the art of being a Pony Express rider. And further in the past were Nate Tobin and all the other symbols of failure that had haunted him. That was all over now for at last he had found himself, his place. It remained only for him to prove his abilities to McCoskey and the job was his permanent property.

It had not been easy to endure the lash of the superintendent's haranguing, but he had stayed with it, stubbornly refusing to lose heart. After taking the oath required of all riders—not to swear or drink liquor while on duty, always to conduct himself as a gentleman and never abuse the horseflesh—he gave himself over to McCoskey, who hammered relentlessly at him day and night.

"Bend your knees, goddammit!" the old man shouted at him time after time when he was having difficulty dismounting from a running horse. "You'll be breaking your legs first out, if'n you don't!"

And Danny Thorpe had learned, just as he had become proficient in handling the *mochila,* an ingenious leather blanket designed to fit over the saddle and upon which four mail pouches had been stitched. It was loaded at each end of the run, was then passed from rider to rider, the trick being to make the exchange without loss of time.

"Nine days from here to St. Joe!" McCoskey had told him. "That's what we're shooting for. We're doing it in ten now— and that's less than half what it takes a letter to come by boat or stagecoach. But we want it done in nine—and we sure as hell can do it if you blasted saddle-warmers'll work at it!"

"Be doing my best," Danny had replied, continually awed by McCoskey's enthusiasm and utter devotion to the cause. "I'll try—"

"Best ain't always good enough. Got to do better. And time's not the only thing important, either. That mail's got to get through; come perdition, it's got to get through! You understand that? No matter what—you get your *mochila* to the next station so's the link rider can keep it moving. We don't take no excuses —none."

"Yes, sir. All I'm asking is a little luck—"

"Luck!" McCoskey exploded. "Man makes his own luck, and don't you forget it! You just mind what I've been telling you and you won't need to depend on something like luck."

And thus it had gone until McCoskey, finally satisfied although frank in declaring himself unconvinced, sent him on his way. Now, with a warm, late fall sun caressing his shoulder, he gained the last rise and looked down on what he hoped would be his new home, Smith's Crossing.

In appearance it left much to be desired. It was no more than a thin scatter of gray, sun- and wind-scoured buildings and pole corrals, completely devoid of vegetation except for a lone tree which stood in solitary dejection in front of the largest structure.

The past was far behind Danny Thorpe when he pulled to a halt at the hitch rack in front of the mud-chinked log-cabin office of the Pony Express and dismounted. He paused for a time, studying the sign above the doorway, a serious-faced miniature of a man dressed in black cord pants, knee-high boots, fringed buckskin coat, and rumpled pork-pie hat. Heavier woolen clothing, suggested by Pat McCoskey, was rolled inside the poncho tied behind the cantle of his saddle.

Hitching at the holstered gun—also borrowed from the line's superintendent—slung at his hip, he crossed to the doorway and entered. Again he halted, allowed his eyes to adjust to the abrupt change of light. It was a large room, he saw, with little furniture that was covered with a thin veneer of yellow dust. Someone was rattling dishes in a room that turned off the primary area and the good, inviting odor of coffee hung in the still, warm air like tantalizing perfume.

"Reckon you're Thorpe, the new rider," a voice said from the left.

Danny wheeled, confronted a squat, dark man with close-set eyes and a friendly grin. "That's me," he said and produced the letter McCoskey had given him. "You'd be Wylie Courtright, the station agent."

Courtright nodded. He opened the letter, glanced at it, thrust it into his pocket. "Had word from Mac that you'd be here today. Good thing. You'll have to make the run in the morning."

"Suits me," Danny said, glancing involuntarily toward the kitchen.

"Expect you're a mite hungry," the agent said, missing nothing. "Sit yourself down and I'll see what I can rustle up. Then we'll talk."

Danny settled himself at a table near a window. From there he could see the corral in which a dozen or so horses stood, hipshot in the pleasant sunlight. All were tough, hard-planed little animals that looked as though they could withstand any amount of punishment heaped upon them. Farther on was the blacksmith shop. The double doors were open and red coals glowed in the forge like evil eyes. Presently the smithy began to work his anvil, the ringing of his hammer clean and clear in the long-reaching quiet.

Courtright reappeared bringing a sandwich of bread and cold beef, cups and a small granite pot of coffee. "Ought to hold you till supper," he said, and sat down opposite. "How's things in Sacramento? Old Mac still pawing the earth like always?"

Danny grinned between bites. "He's sure one for the book, all right."

"Don't think he'd be satisfied even with that feller on the winged horse," the agent said, wagging his head. "But he's got the right idea. Training he gives you boys is what's making this mail-line work."

"Thought I was a pretty fair hand with a horse until I come up against him," Danny said. "What's my other home station and how far is it?"

"Red Valley—and it's about a hundred and seventy miles off. You got eleven relay stations in between."

"A hundred and seventy miles," Danny murmured. "Quite a piece."

"For a fact. Most home stations are about a hundred, more or less. This stretch's the longest on the line. That's why we have trouble keeping a man on it. But it ain't too bad. Mostly flat country and easy going."

"Any Indian trouble?"

"Not lately. Country's too dang Godforsaken even for them I expect. Personally, I don't blame a man for quitting it."

"I'll stick," Danny said, "if I make the grade."

Courtright was silent for a moment. Then, "Don't think you'll have any trouble doing that. Just keep remembering that mail's got to come through on time—but mostly it's got to come through. But I reckon Mac told you all that."

"He sure did—plenty loud and often."

"That's sort of extra special now. You're going to be carrying some mighty important mail in your *mochila* on your return trip."

Danny frowned, poured himself a second cup of coffee. "Important?"

"Yeh, the election returns. People'll be real anxious to know who won—Lincoln or that feller Douglas."

Danny had forgotten all about the national election, not that it meant anything particular to him. A man had to keep on living and working no matter who sat in the White House.

"People like us maybe don't pay much attention to things like that," Courtright said, reading his thoughts, "but these here big businessmen set a pile by who gets the job. Heard some of them say they're mighty certain we'll go to war if Lincoln wins."

Danny showed his surprise. "Pshaw!" he scoffed. "War with who? We licked the Mexicans—"

"War with the South," the agent said quietly. "Sure does seem trouble's brewing down there. Be a terrible thing was we to get to fightin' betwixt ourselves."

"For certain," Danny agreed. "What time in the morning do I start this run?"

"Three-thirty. You can figure on old Bob being here right on the nose. You're allowed two minutes to make the change and get going."

"Won't need it."

"Don't expect you will. And be wearing that gun. Some of the boys don't pack a weapon but you ought to on this stretch."

"Thought you said—"

"Ain't thinking so much about Indians, I'm just thinking you ought to go armed. Been more strangers moseying through here lately. Duded-up city fellers. Was three here only a couple of days ago. Ain't got no idea what they're up to—maybe nothing. But just as well you keep your eyes peeled."

"I'll do it," Danny said. He glanced about the room. "Now, if you'll point out my bunk quarters, I think I'll get me some sleep. Three-thirty comes powerful early."

"Right over there," Courtright said, waving at a door in the opposite wall. "I'll wake you for supper. You can meet the rest of the folks then."

"Fine," Danny murmured, rising and starting across the floor. "That'll be fine."

Excitement was having its strong way with him that next morning as he stood before the crackling fire in the rock fireplace and sipped at his coffee. He was eager to be in the saddle and gone, impatient to open up this new life that lay before him. He grinned at Courtright, who winked back knowingly. Only the agent and the two hostlers were up and about at that early hour. He had met the blacksmith, his helper, the cook, and two or three other employees the evening before. Theirs were the routine jobs about the place and there was no need for them to be abroad now.

Courtright, his easygoing shape slouched in the doorway, consulted the thick, nickel-silver watch he carried. "About due," he said and crossed to where Danny stood. "When you get going, just leave things up to the horses," he said. "They know this here route better'n any man."

Danny nodded. He finished his coffee, placed the empty cup on the mantel, and walked to the window. It was a clear night, silvered by a star-studded sky. Opening the hinged sash he listened into the deep silence. The distant, fast beat of a running horse was a faint drumming in the quiet.

"He's coming," he said and started for the door.

"No hurry," Courtright replied, shaking his head. "Be another five, six minutes."

Danny did not pause, impatience now prodding him mercilessly. "Want to be ready," he said, and stepped out into the yard.

The station agent grinned understandingly. He reached for his sheepskin-lined jacket, drew it on. Picking up the three letters that were to be added to the mail pouch, he followed Thorpe into the brisk night. He halted where Danny was inspecting the gear on the horse readied for him by the hostlers.

"Eastern stuff," he said, thrusting the letters at Thorpe. "Goes in the right front pocket."

Danny bucked his head. Three of the compartments in the *mochila* were padlocked, contained the important mail placed in them at the beginning of the run, and could not be opened until the agent or proper official at the finish of the line—in this case St. Joe—produced the key. The fourth pocket, at the rider's right knee, was left open for pickup and delivery along the way.

Danny tucked the letters inside his shirt. He would put them in their proper pocket after he was in the saddle, not waste time doing it before he mounted. It was another of the small, seemingly insignificant things Pat McCoskey had taught him to do, all of which, added together, meant several minutes of time saved in the over-all run.

Satisfied his horse was ready, Danny walked deeper into the yard. The hoofbeats were louder now and throwing his glance down the road, he caught sight of the oncoming rider.

A thrill of pride raced through him. The man was hunched forward over his mount. A scarf about his neck whipped out behind him, like some brave banner, waving its defiance to all who would see. The horse was running full tilt, head extended, mane and tail flowing in shimmering waves. His legs were no more than a blur in the semidarkness. Danny's heart bulged; this was for him—this was the sort of life he sought, must have. A man could be proud of being a Pony Express rider; and one he would be—or die trying.

The waiting horse began to prance nervously, anxious to pick up the race. One of the hostlers swore softly, affectionately, began to lead the animal about in a tight circle to relieve the tension. Suddenly the rider was thundering into the yard. Danny had a glimpse of the man's taut features as he came off his horse; he saw the oblong shape of the *mochila* as it was tossed to him. He caught it neatly, flung it over his saddle with practiced accuracy, and vaulted into place. In the next instant he was surging off into the night.

It had been a good exchange, a fast one, and Pat McCoskey would have been proud of him, he thought as he rushed on. And then he grinned wryly. He doubted if anything would ever completely satisfy the old superintendent. To him perfection was merely a step to an even higher goal.

Jamming the three letters Wylie Courtright had given him into the *mochila*'s pocket and closing the spring snap, Danny looked ahead. The road was a faint white ribbon curving off through a dark border of weeds, grass, and other growth. A great wave of happiness rolled through him and he took a long, deep breath, of the sharp, clean air. He was in the saddle—on his way; it was real now—he was a Pony Express rider.

Or . . . almost, he thought soberly, cautioning his soaring spirits. He still must prove himself to McCoskey. He must make the run over and over again—do it right. He must heed the superintendent's instructions, remember his own oath, not forget the things Courtright had told him. He must be on time, get the mail through—and make no mistakes. It was a big order, but he would do it. Nothing must prevent his making good.

He settled lower on the saddle as the buckskin pounded on through the night. Miles fled by. Stars overhead began to pale

and fade. The scraggly growth and irregular-shaped rock formations grew more distinct. A jack rabbit scurried across the road,
was quickly lost in the brush. They rounded a turn and abruptly
the first relay station lay before him, a small weathered scar in
the wide emptiness. It seemed hardly possible they had covered
so much ground or that he had been riding for almost two hours.

He swept into the yard, the face of the hostler standing ready
with his fresh mount only a soft-edged blur in the half light.
Grasping the *mochila* in the manner Pat McCoskey had taught
him, he prepared to make the change. It went off smoothly,
without lost motion, as he had hoped, and in fleeting seconds
he was again on the road, this time astride a barrel-bodied pinto
gelding that ran as though all hell and its proprietor were at his
heels.

An hour later, as he began to climb a long, gentle slope,
sunrise caught him, bringing with it a brisk, cutting wind that
struck deep into his bones and made him wish for heavier
clothing. But the wind had died by the time he made the next
relay point, and when the third change had been accomplished,
and without incident, he found himself unreasonably warm and
removed his jacket.

Noon passed but he felt no hunger, just a gradually increasing
stiffness that claimed his muscles, sent shooting pains up his back
and through his shoulders. He had thought himself accustomed
to hard riding, hours upon end; he was realizing now, as
McCoskey had warned him, that a great difference lay between
just riding a horse and forking a Pony Express mount steadily,
hour after hour, at a dead run.

The country became more desolate and the loneliness of the
land began to weigh on him. He tried not to think of that, to
dwell only upon the good fortune that had come his way—that
would remain his if he could successfully prove his worth and
ability. It was all like a dream, a vague, happy dream—one he
hoped would never end.

He received a surprise near dark when he reached the final
relay station, found a girl waiting with his remount. She smiled
sweetly at him as he lunged past her and leaped onto the saddle.

Later he could not recall whether he had smiled back or not. He would make a point of doing so on the return trip, he told himself. She had been pretty and it would be nice to know someone along the trail.

Immediately he remembered that Pony Express riders were supposed to remain unmarried, and he guessed he'd better forget about her. It could lead to problems and nothing—*nothing*—was going to interfere with his job.

It was shortly after seven-thirty when he pulled into Red Valley station and flung the *mochila* to the waiting link rider. Every bone and muscle in his body was crying, and he staggered uncertainly as he started toward the door. He scarcely heard the greeting of the agent, and shook the man's hand woodenly. He was hungry, too, but that would have to wait; first he wanted only to stretch out on a bed for a few minutes.

And then as he passed through the doorway into the main room where an evening meal was being placed on a table for him by the agent's wife, he came to a stunned halt. Standing before the fireplace, watching him with narrowed eyes, were two men. Danny Thorpe's heart skipped a beat. It was Pete Newton and Bill Stanger. Nugget Nate Tobin's avengers had found him after all.

Weariness dropped from Danny's shoulders, was forgotten. Worry and the old familiar feeling of hopelessness stiffened him. He stared at the pair, incongruous in the rough surroundings in their tight-fitting suits, derby hats, and button shoes.

"What do you want?"

His voice sounded strange to his own ears. It was tight, oddly husky. He watched Bill Stanger take a step forward, lift his hands, palms outward, in a conciliatory gesture.

"Want? Why, nothing, Shorty. We're just passing through, a couple of pilgrims on our way east."

"That's right," Newton chimed in. "Pilgrims, that's us."

"You're not looking for me?" Danny asked, bluntly.

Stanger appeared surprised. "For you—oh, you mean on account of that race-track business? Nate's done forgot that. All he wanted was to learn you a lesson. When you hightailed it, I reckon it satisfied him."

Danny considered that for several moments. It did seem unlikely Tobin would go to such lengths to even the score with him. And how could he and his thugs have known he was working for the Pony Express, or, more particularly, that he was on that exact run?

Stanger said: "How long you been carrying the mail?"

"First time out," Danny replied, his anxiety beginning to ease. Apparently the two men had no interest in him.

"Like it?"

"Real fine," Danny replied and turned to the table. He had changed his mind; he would have something to eat before he climbed into bed.

"Beats whacking them broomtails around a track, eh?"

"Sure does," Danny said, and settled onto his chair. He raised a cup of coffee to his lips, drank gratefully. Newton spoke from across the room.

"You heading back west in the morning?"

Danny nodded. A vague doubt concerning the presence of the two men was seeping into his mind. Perhaps they were no longer interested in exacting vengeance upon him for what Tobin considered a double-cross, but there could be something else. They were much too friendly, and they were asking a lot of questions.

He puzzled over the problem while he ate, now and then casting covert glances at the pair, still standing before the fireplace. What could they be planning? The Pony Express carried little, if any, money; robbery would not be the motive, especially where a big-time gambler like Nate Tobin was involved. It had to be something else—if there were reasons for his suspicion. He finally concluded it best to simply remain quiet but keep his eyes open.

The station agent came in, sat down across the table. "Name's Ruskin. Charlie Ruskin," he said. "Didn't get much chance to introduce myself because of your friends. You'd be Danny Thorpe?"

"Right. And they're not what I'd call my friends."

Ruskin smiled, not exactly understanding. "Just figured they was from the way you were talking. Anyway, thought you'd like knowing you made the run in sixteen hours, assuming you got off on time."

"On the nose," Danny said, then added: "Is that good?"

"Just what it's figured for—sixteen hours. Has been done in less, and a few times when it took longer." The agent rose to his feet, a tall, friendly man with deep lines in his face. "Expect you're ready to hit the hay. First time out a rider learns he has muscles he never dreamed of."

Danny nodded and got to his feet. "What time do I leave in the morning?"

"Six o'clock, if nothing goes wrong. Door to the left is your room. Anything you need?"

"Only sleep," Thorpe said and moved to his quarters.

It seemed to him that he had scarcely pulled the quilts about his neck when Charlie Ruskin was shaking his shoulder.

"Five o'clock. Time you were up and around."

Danny got to his feet groggily, and then as the sharp, cold air sliced through the fog in his brain, he dressed hurriedly and went into the lobby. He ate quickly, gulping two cups of steaming black coffee, then hastened outside to inspect his horse. The hostler had just finished saddling the animal, a half-wild little sorrel that nipped ferociously at the stableman each time he came within range.

"He's a bad one," the hustler said, "but faster'n a turpentined cat on the road. Figured that's the kind you'd be wanting."

Danny said, "What I like," then paused, realizing there was deeper meaning to the man's words. "Some reason why I ought to have a fast horse?"

The hostler glanced up. "Sure. Every rider on the line'll be pouring it on. We'll be carrying the 'lection returns."

There was pride in the man's tone. Danny grinned at him. "Danged if I hadn't forgot that!"

"Be a big feather in the company's cap, was we to get the news to Frisco in record time."

And in mine, Danny thought and walked away. The sky to the east was a dull pearl gray. It looked like he would have good weather. He swung his eyes about the yard, back to the station. There was no sign of Newton or Bill Stanger. Wondering about them, he retreated to the main room. Charlie Ruskin was at his desk.

"Nothing for you to carry on," he said, looking up. "Probably a good thing. Likely you'll be loaded."

"Probably," Danny said. "That pair—the ones you called my friends—what happened to them?"

"Rode out. About an hour ago."

"Which way?"

"Headed east, I reckon. Leastwise, that's what they said. Never paid them no mind. Why?"

He guessed he had figured them wrong. Danny sighed. Whatever it was they were up to evidently had nothing to do with him. He shrugged. "No reason. Was just asking."

He went back to the yard, crossed to where the hostler stood with the sorrel. His mind was now on the job that lay before him. He wondered if he could better the time usually required to cover the distance between the two home stations. Sixteen hours was standard, Ruskin had said. Maybe if he worked at it he could trim it down to fifteen. He would be on a good horse at the start. If he pushed him and his successive remounts hard, he just might turn the trick. A fast time record could go far in cinching the job for him.

He checked the sorrel's gear again, found it to his liking. A few minutes later the pound of hoofs announced the coming of the link rider. Tension gripping him as before, Danny took his position, made ready to receive the *mochila* and continue the relay.

The rider entered the yard in a rush. He left his saddle in a long leap, sent the leather blanket with its bulging pockets sailing through the fading darkness at Danny.

"Lincoln won!" he shouted. "Pass it along!"

Danny spun to the sorrel, already moving out. He flung the *mochila* across the saddle, lost precious moments yanking it into position because of the fractious horse, and vaulted aboard. The sorrel was at top speed before he reached the trail.

Danny swore softly to himself. It had been a poor changeover; the horse had been jumpy and too anxious. He would remember that the next time the fiery little red was given him. But actually the time loss was small and the horse, seemingly to know he was at fault, was doing all in his power to make up for his error. He was running hard, his hoofs beating so rapid a tattoo that the sound blended into a steady drum roll.

He gained the first relay station without the sorrel breaking stride, and he left the horse regretfully, wishing he might have him or his equal to ride the rest of the long journey. The girl was not in the yard as he made the exchange and he yelled, "Lincoln got elected!" at the old man who stood ready with his fresh mount. The man called back: "How's that?" but Danny was surging away and there was no time in which to repeat the news.

He was in the low-foothill country now, an area where the trail wound through a maze of bubble-like formations covered by thin brush and rock. It was the slowest section of the route and as the buckskin hammered his way up and down the grades and around the numberless curves, Danny saw the lead the sorrel had given him melt away.

He raised his eyes. A long slope faced him. It was one of the few straight stretches to be found in the hills and it led to a naked summit that rose several hundred feet above the surrounding land. Beyond it, he recalled, lay a wide swale. Once over the rim the buckskin could do better.

Suddenly the horse paused in stride. Danny saw first a puff of white smoke off to the side of the road. Then came the dry slap of a gunshot. The buckskin's head went down, then snapped up as his legs folded beneath him. Danny felt himself soaring through space. Abruptly the ground came up and met him with solid, sickening force.

He fought his way back to consciousness slowly. His head ached and there was a stabbing pain in his left shoulder. He became aware of voices and opened his eyes. He lay full length in a sandy wash a few yards from the road. The luckless buckskin, dead, was just beyond. The *mochila,* the contents of its unlocked pocket strewn about, was close by. A newspaper, unfolded, its bold black headlines proclaiming the election of Abraham Lincoln to the Presidency, had been examined and tossed aside.

"How long you stalling around here?"

Danny started. Pete Newton's voice! Ignoring the pain that raced through him, he twisted about to where he could see better. The two men were a dozen paces to his right. They had shed their city clothing, were now dressed for hard riding. Newton was tightening the cinch of his saddle.

"Not long. Got to get rid of him and that mail. Then I'll be coming."

Newton hesitated. "Could lend you a hand."

"Better not take the time. Sooner we get the word passed to Nate, the better. Shape that nag of mine's in, I'd slow you down, anyway."

Pete Newton finished his chore, swung onto his horse. "Maybe you ought to just leave things as they are. Ain't so sure it's smart to go fooling around with the U.S. mail—"

Stanger swore impatiently. "Quit fretting about it! Let me take care of my end. You get the word to Tobin. He stands to make a pile of cash on this deal and I sure wouldn't want to be the one who knocked him out of it."

Newton muttered something and pulled his horse about, headed for the road. "So long," he called back over his shoulder. Stanger only nodded.

Understanding came quickly to Danny Thorpe. Tobin was gambling heavily on the election. By knowing the results in advance and also delaying the delivery of that information, he stood to make a fortune. Stanger and Newton had been dispatched to accomplish that end.

A hopelessness settled over Danny as frustration gripped him. Why did it have to happen to him? Why did Tobin's thugs have to choose the very run he was on? Was it because he was a green rider on the job? Or was it that such things always seem to come his way?

That was it, he concluded bitterly. That—and the fact that the run he was on was the longest, most forsaken and desolate stretch in the entire line. Such made it easy for them to work their plan. *Let something go haywire—and it'll end up in my lap,* he moaned softly.

Through despairing eyes he watched Newton strike off westward. Stanger, too, kept his gaze on the departing man for a time, then turned, walked leisurely toward Danny. His jaw was set and his hand rested on the butt of the pistol hanging at his hip. Danny felt his throat tighten. He would have no chance against a killer such as Bill Stanger; all he could do was lie still, feign unconsciousness. Maybe something would turn up—a bit of good luck. . . .

Luck!

The word caught in Danny Thorpe's mind, began to glow vividly. What was it old Pat McCoskey had said? *A man makes his own luck.* It was true, he realized. It was wrong to just sit back, take what fate threw at him—and not fight. When a man fought for his rights, he changed things, made them go his way. Maybe he failed in the trying, maybe he even died—but at least he'd had a hand in his own destiny.

A hard core of denial, of brittle resentment, began to build within Danny Thorpe. He still had his pistol. Bill Stanger and Newton held him in such low esteem they had not bothered to remove it. But it was under him and he could not reach it without moving. He dared not do that. Let Stanger think him still unconscious; against a killer like him it was necessary to lessen the odds in some way.

Stanger halted a step to his left, a tower of intimidation staring down at the small man. Danny could feel his cold eyes drilling into the back of his head. Stanger was considering his next move. Danny waited, utterly motionless. After an eternity Stanger turned, walked to where the opened newspaper lay, something apparently capturing his attention.

Danny gathered his strength. He must act now or forever be

lost. Ignoring the pain in his shoulder, he came to a crouching position, drew his weapon. Stanger was still reading, his back partly turned. A faint dizziness swept through Danny, and then a sudden wave of doubt. He brushed both away, sprang upright.

At the sound of crunching sand Stanger whirled. His mouth dropped open in surprise, then hardened. A broad, patronizing grin spread over his dark face.

"Now, Shorty, you know you're too little to go messing around with a gun," he said in a dry, sarcastic voice. "Better you drop it," he added, and reached for his own weapon.

Danny fired once. Stanger jolted as the bullet smashed into his chest. Again surprise blanked his features. He frowned and abruptly caved in, went full length onto the warming sand.

Danny wasted no time checking the effect of his single bullet. He spun, dropped to his knees beside the *mochila*. Scooping up the spilled mail, he crammed it into its pocket, snapped the flap into place. Rising, he ran to Stanger's horse, threw the leather blanket into position, and mounted. Spurring the long-legged bay roughly, he got him back to the road and struck out hard for the next relay station.

The bay should last that far, he reasoned, rubbing at his throbbing shoulder. Then, with a fresh horse he would have a good chance of overtaking Pete Newton. He had lost a good half hour, possibly more, so he could forget his hopes of making a record run. But he would get the mail through.

The bay began to tire after the first five miles of steady running. Danny slacked up on the reins. It would be folly to run the horse into the ground. He must nurse the brute along, keep him going even if it resolved into a slow trot. Anything would be faster than being on foot.

He wondered if Pete Newton's horse was in the same condition, guessed it likely was. A new thought entered his mind: Tobin had probably set up a relay of his own. Courtright had mentioned three strangers. Two of them would have been Stanger and Newton. The third was likely stationed somewhere farther along the route—and if that was true then there would be others strung out all the way to San Francisco. Overtaking and halting Newton loomed more important to Danny Thorpe at that realization.

He reached the relay point with the bay near exhaustion. The hostler stared at him as he came off the saddle and leaped onto his remount.

"You're late!" the man shouted.

Danny shook his head, called back: "Lincoln won!" and raced on down the road.

He felt better now with a fresh horse under him. He wished there had been time enough to inquire about Newton, ask the hostler if he had noted a passing rider, but he could not afford the delay. Arriving so far behind schedule was going to be a mark against him, could even place his hopes for permanent assignment in jeopardy. It was best he recover all the time possible. He would see Pete Newton soon enough. The sorrel he now rode was covering the ground with amazing speed—or else it seemed so after the slow grind on Stanger's worn bay.

He caught a glimpse of Tobin's man a half hour later. Newton was topping out a rise a quarter mile distant. He heard the beat of the sorrel and Danny watched him twist about, could visualize the surprise that would cover his face.

Immediately Newton began to flog his horse, moving then at an easy gallop. Danny considered the man's frantic efforts to pull away, at least to maintain his lead. But his mount was no match for the fresh sorrel. The gap closed rapidly. When no more than a hundred yards separated them, Newton resorted to his pistol and began to shoot. Danny had hoped it would not come to gunplay; the shock of having killed Bill Stanger was still a heavy sickness within him. Yet he knew deep in his mind that it was useless to hope; men such as Newton and Stanger recognized no other solution when cornered.

He drew his own weapon, bided his time. The distance between them was still too great for a handgun. The sorrel thundered on. The spread decreased. Newton, reloading, opened up again. Danny heard the angry whirr of bullets. He was near enough. He leveled off on Newton, aiming for the man's shoulder, squeezed the trigger twice. Newton bucked on his saddle, heaved to one side. Immediately his horse slowed, began to veer away. Newton's gun fell to the ground, sending up a spurt of dry dust when it struck. The horse stopped. Newton folded, clung to the saddle horn.

Danny, not slackening his speed, drew abreast. He threw a searching glance at the man, saw that he was only wounded. He sighed in relief, shouted: "I'll send somebody back for you!" and rushed on.

He was feeling better now. He had halted Tobin's makeshift relay, checked his scheme to fleece a lot of people—a scheme in which the Pony Express had been an innocent participant. And he had won over himself. He smiled grimly at that thought; yes, he had won the battle—but likely he had lost the war.

He swept into the next relay station, paused only long enough to shout instructions concerning Pete Newton, and then hurried on determined to make up as much lost time as possible. But a mile is a mile and a horse can do only so much. When he rode into Smith's Crossing late that night, he knew he was nearly an hour behind schedule.

Weary, dejected, expecting the worst, he entered the station. Explanations would mean nothing; they would sound like alibis. To be sure, he could produce the reason for his delay. He could have Newton brought in, but Newton, of course, would deny everything—as would Nate Tobin. And Stanger was dead. It would help little anyway. Other Pony Express riders had such problems, dealt with them, and still managed to maintain their schedules. It was a part of the job and expected of them.

"Running a mite behind, ain't you, boy?"

Pat McCoskey's raspy voice cut him like a whip. He hauled up sharply, stared at the superintendent while his spirits sagged lower. McCoskey had ridden out to check on him, to see what sort of a job he was doing. On that he would base his decision as to whether Danny Thorpe became a permanent employee or not.

"Afraid I am," Danny said miserably. "Sorry about it."

"Sorry!" McCoskey rumbled. "What're you being sorry for? Far as I'm concerned, you done fine. New men generally get all fired up trying to impress everybody about how good they are. Do their best to make the run faster'n it ever been done before. Glad to see you ain't that kind. Show's you'll make a good rider."

Danny's eyes filled with disbelief. A grin cracked his lips. Then he sobered. He had to be honest about it. "Yes, sir, but I was—" he began and then checked his words as Wylie Courtright frowned, shook his head meaningfully at him.

"Time average was real good," the station agent said, stepping up to McCoskey's side. "Figures out a little more than sixteen and a half hours each way. And you had a heavy *mochila*. Can't ask for much better from a new man."

"And I ain't," McCoskey added, smiling, something he was seldom guilty of. "Hope you like it here with Wylie, son. It's going to be your regular station."

Danny could only bob his head happily. Something was blocking his throat, choking him, causing his heart to sing with a joy he had never known. He couldn't put it into words even to himself, but a wonderful thing had happened; Danny Thorpe had at last found himself and his place.

Rough Road to Royal Gorge

BY C. S. PARK

Following shortly upon the demise of the Pony Express, dooming with it the great freight strings of Waddell and Majors and vast skeins of stage line woven by Butterworth and Halliday, came the railroads. The "transcontinental," as dear to the superlative in American nature in its time as a later Panama Canal or race to the moon, curiously exerted less influence upon Western development than a whole rash of more humble shirt-tail cousins. The fabled "iron horse" was most often a rusty, cantankerous, narrow-gauge mule or donkey. Shamelessly, often scandalously subsidized with public lands and funds and used as political footballs by more than one administration, the U.P. and the Central Pacific shared the distinction of "first." And they made a few not-too-deserving men exceedingly rich. But the real penetration of and service to the frontier were achieved by far lesser lines. Forced to survive by their own efforts, they fought desperate battles, often with inspired chicanery, for every mile of track and dollar of potential revenue. —T.W.B.

GENERAL William Barstow Strong's message caught up with Morley in La Junta, Colorado. The urgent order, via coded wire, read: "Take Royal Gorge at once and hold it until reinforcements arrive." But there was nothing to tell Morley *how* to do it. To get to the Gorge meant that he had to cross enemy lines, and to hold it required a substantial party of rough and ready fighters.

He wired back to the General at El Moro, down near the New Mexico border, "Leaving immediately," commandeered a work train, and left La Junta in a cloud of hissing steam and thundering black smoke belching from the balloon-shaped smokestack.

In the Raton headquarters of General William Jackson Palmer, an aide deciphered Morley's last message, eavesdropped from the telegraph wire. Palmer said, "Well, are we ready to leave?" and the aide replied: "With a hundred tough and eager men and their equipment, sir. I will start them north right now."

So began the furious race for the Royal Gorge of the Arkansas River and its rich prize of booming Leadville's shipping business —a race between one man and a hundred!

General Strong, general manager of the Atchison, Topeka, and Santa Fe, had earlier asked for a special train to carry men up to Canon City at the mouth of the Gorge. But Denver and Rio Grande, headed by General Palmer, owned the track over which the Santa Fe people would have to travel. D&RG also wanted the Gorge, in which there was room for only one railroad. Naturally, the request was refused. And Strong, livid with humiliation, rage, and frustration, had no alternative but to assign the impossible task of getting men into the Gorge first to one of his civil engineers, William Raymond Morley.

Morley received a second message at Granada, east of Pueblo. It read tersely: "Reinforcements delayed. Good luck." And I'll need it, Morley thought. He was not a large man, but there was a "no compromise" angle to his wide-brimmed hat, in the slant of his broad shoulders, in his direct gaze. He wore a working construction engineer's boots, Levis, and a flannel shirt.

"May get rain," the locomotive engineer shouted. "You bring a slicker?"

"Didn't have time to dress for the occasion," Morley replied.

Swaying to the rocking motion of the racing engine, Morley considered his course. He pictured two lines crossing at right angles. The point where they crossed was Pueblo. At the bottom of the perpendicular line were Raton and El Moro; at the top, Denver. At the right end of the horizontal line was La Junta; at the opposite end, Canon City. Denver and Rio Grande's invasion party, headed by their chief construction engineer, McMurtrie, was steaming north on their narrow-gauge track. The heavy drivers of Morley's engine were pounding Santa Fe's standard-gauge rails. But from Pueblo west to Canon City, the

D&RG owned the tracks, upon which Santa Fe's wide-span wheels would not fit. And one of Morley's problems—transportation—would begin there. Another would be the lack of communications: west of Pueblo the telegraph line to Canon City was not yet completed.

He came out of his planning when the engineer yelled: "Git, you varmint!" and pulled the whistle cord. A slinking coyote streaked across in front of the cowcatcher. The fireman shouted: "I'll 'git' him!" and swept a carbine from a rack, cocked it, and pulled the trigger. Nothing happened. He quickly levered up a shell, fired, and the coyote was bowled over. The fireman said in Morley's ear, "Never keep anything in the chamber. Always forget." But to Morley an "unloaded" gun was the worst kind— if you kept it loaded, you at least knew that it was and you treated it with due respect.

They pounded into the Pueblo yards at five in the evening, with the April sun hanging like an ominous red eye over the horizon. Morley hurried to the D&RG depot, where the division superintendent told him bluntly: "You people hornswoggled us out of the Raton Pass. So does it make sense that I should supply you with a special so you can beat us to the Gorge as you did to Raton?" He indicated a locomotive puffing on a siding. "They notified me two hours ago. That's waiting to tie onto our own special, loaded with men and tools for Canon City. This time Santa Fe will be eating *our* dust!"

There was no use arguing with him. Morley said, "There's more than one way to skin a cat," and departed thoughtfully, wondering if in this case there really was. But the superintendent's own remarks reminded him that in the case of Raton Pass, General Strong had found a way.

Events leading up to the Royal Gorge were similar, he thought, to those that led up to the capture of Raton Pass by the Santa Fe: Denver and Rio Grande had been building south from Pueblo, and every one knew that General Palmer intended to go through Raton Pass, the only practical way through the Raton Mountains on the New Mexico line. But General Strong, quietly investigating, secured a charter to lay tracks in southern Colorado and

New Mexico. D&RG spies learned about this, but were not overly concerned. As General Palmer put it: "Logic decrees that you begin building in one place and end in another, doesn't it? Santa Fe track is already laid as far as Pueblo. We can safely assume that the track laying will begin there. They will have to have some other way over the Ratons than through the Pass." But in his quiet way, Strong had learned that Palmer had failed to do an essential thing: under the act of March 5, 1875—two years before—it was necessary to file a plat of the proposed route in the land office, and Palmer had overlooked it. So Strong caused a quick, secret survey to be made of Raton Pass, filed his plat, and then began building *in* the Pass. It was D&RG that had to find another way across the mountains. And since then, enmity such as shown by the division superintendent had existed between the two companies.

A train, Morley thought, is not the only mode of transportation, but it was the only practical way to take a crew up to Canon City, in time. But a single man in a light buggy—or on horseback?

Now a curious circumstance conspired against hurrying Morley: every livery stable he was able to reach was temporarily out of horses! "It's the big livestock auction out at the county fair," one operator explained. "It's only half a mile out of town, but you know how these cowmen are—they have to have a horse even to cross a street from one drinking place to another."

Standing in front of a saloon where several horses were tied at the rail, Morley figured he might steal one. Then he had a mental picture of a posse pouring out of Pueblo on his trail, and somewhere between here and Canon City, himself dangling at the end of a long rope slung over the limb of a tall aspen. He did not dismiss the idea entirely from his mind, but it would have to be a last resort.

Each minute lost standing here in thought was a minute gained by the Denver and Rio Grande, though. When a big-hatted man walked out of the saloon and swung up on a long-legged sorrel, Morley said, "Mister, I work for the Santa Fe and I need to get to Canon City in a hurry. I'll give you two hundred dollars for that horse."

The man turned and stared down. "Mister," he answered, "I work for the D&RG. And I wouldn't give the Santa Fe the sweat off this horse's rump for twice that amount!" Then he spat on the ground close to Morley's feet and rode off. The deliberate act reddened Morley's neck and ruffled his temper, but he had learned a lesson. If Santa Fe had friends in Pueblo, he didn't have time to look for them.

He hastened into the saloon. There was a poker game in progress. Five men and the bartender were deeply engrossed in it. Morley announced: "I'll pay two hundred dollars for that black at the hitch rail."

A young fellow with a meager pile of chips in front of him held out his hand, cupped. "His name is King William and I hate to part with him, but you couldn't have come at a better time. Make it three hundred and I'll throw in that silver-mounted saddle."

This was a piece of luck that Morley needed—now to "ride" it. He hurried out before the young gambler could win the pot and want to buy the horse back. That red sun had gone down behind the Wet Mountains, leaving only an orange hue in the western sky when Morley ran the black out of Pueblo. He found that King William had a rocking-chair gait and a deep bottom. But at the edge of town Morley pulled him to a walk—it wouldn't do to run him off his legs. There were forty-three rough and weary miles to cover and he knew he was in for a tough time—he hadn't ridden much, and then for only short distances, since his college days at Iowa State, sixteen years before.

At seventeen he had marched with Sherman. The poor planning of Georgia's turnpikes had made the march harder and spurred his natural interest in civil engineering. After the war he enrolled in a course at the Iowa school, where he fell in love with the most beautiful girl on campus. He was so poor that he had to milk the president's cow to help pay his tuition, and for lack of better clothing still wore parts of his Army uniform, but he resolved to make her fall in love with him, too.

Sometime later her father said to her, "Ada, you can have your pick of any man in this school, so why choose one who is your social and intellectual inferior?" He was Judge McPherson, and she usually listened to his advice, but this time she only said, "He won't always be, Father."

Morley wasn't quite twenty when he graduated, went to Denver, and joined a survey party at the lowest kind of labor— brush-cutting. He had an eager interest in the work of everyone in the party. That irritated another brush-cutter, a large and burly man, who charged: "You're just trying to make time with the boss." To which Morley replied, "There's something wrong with that?" It wasn't long before the other brush-cutter picked a fight, and Morley took a terrific beating before he was knocked out. When he had recovered, a day or so later, he jumped the other man, and when he found he couldn't finish the fight even though he had the other groggy, he picked up a pick handle and floored him with that. They all left him alone from then on, and five weeks later William Raymond Morley was the head surveyor in that party, and the brush-cutter he had whipped was his rodman and best friend. So it was as a rising young engineer and a promising leader of men that he went back to Iowa and married Ada McPherson.

The political struggle over the routing of a railroad in 1872 put a temporary end to what was already a brilliant engineering career. Morley temporarily took over management of an estate near Cimarron. That didn't keep him busy enough, so he bought a newspaper. Cimarron was a rough, politics-ridden town, and Morley tried to make it a better place to live in with an editorial crusade. Threats against his life became commonplace.

At one morning's late breakfast Ada finally told him, "Rayme, I don't like this country. I always have this dreadful feeling of impending violence." The years and four children had done her no harm, Morley thought. She was still an Iowa girl with long legs and golden hair. He realized that she had reason for her seldom-spoken dread; besides exposing the local crooked politicians in the pages of his paper, he and a fair-minded Methodist minister had written a series of articles about them which appeared in the New York *Sun*. Subsequently, the minister was assassinated, and it was reasonable to believe that Morley would be next. He had a blistering editorial to write, and ordinarily would have been in his office an hour ago, but he hated to leave Ada in her present mood. He said, "Isn't it a condition of mind? Do such feelings have a place on a peaceful day like this?"

From where he sat he could look through the window that was open to the morning breeze, the hum of insects, the songs of birds, and he could see their youngest, a happy towheaded girl of three, seated on the doorstep eating a piece of bread and sugar. Then there was a sudden loud shout outside, and Morley sprang to the door as a man standing in a light rig whipped a running horse wildly into the yard. Morley snatched up his little girl. A cursing rider on a galloping dun pounded out of the dust, shot the driver of the rig in the back, whirled, and raced off. The murdered man fell into the dirt as limply as a dropped sack of wheat. Dust and bluebottle flies settled over him and the bread and sugar in the wide-eyed little girl's hands. For ten horror-filled seconds there was only the sad sighing of the dry morning wind around the corners of the house. Then Ada whisked the little girl out of Morley's arms, and he hurried into the yard to meet an approaching rider from whose vest a silver star reflected the bright sun.

This sheriff was a hulking man with green eyes and a too-ready smile. He was a member of the faction that Morley had been actively attacking in the pages of his Cimarron *News and Press*. "Go after him!" Morley said.

The sheriff dismounted heavily. "That could be Clay Allison, and I'm not in a mood to commit suicide. He and some of his friends just shot up Cimarron and wrecked your office." He looked at the dead man. "He must have thought your printer was you." He sighed. "Well, let's get him into the rig and I'll take him back to town."

So they lifted the fallen man, whose only sin was that he worked for Morley, into the wagon. The sheriff drove out of the yard with his horse shambling along behind, and Morley went into the house. He knew that if there were to be reprisals they wouldn't come from this cowardly sheriff's office. And Morley felt that Allison had been paid by the machine to wreck his office and even kill him. Anger came when he was digging to the bottom of an old trunk. It made his hands tremble as he lifted out a package swathed in red flannel and carried it to the kitchen table. He was unwrapping it when Ada walked in and asked in a shocked tone: "What are you doing?"

She had a fear of guns, Morley had his own phobia about the "unloaded" kind, and so he had stored this one away so that it wouldn't bother either of them. He said, "Clean it! Load it! And go after Allison!"

"With guns, Rayme? I know you aren't afraid, but what about us? How can I go on raising our family under these conditions?"

He heard the plaintive, desperate note in her voice, and it made him pause. There was more involved here than just himself. This became a long moment of decision, and once he had reached it, there was no looking back.

"Start packing," he said. "There are more railroads to be built!"

Occupation of the Royal Gorge in the Grand Canyon of the Arkansas River was a preliminary step in the building of a railroad. Morley alternately walked, trotted, and loped the rangy black along a dark and unfamiliar road that wound and dipped and climbed toward the Gorge. Building railroads was his life. There had been mighty challenges to test his genius—the scenic Glorieta Pass, the La Veta Pass, the steep Raton Pass. All challenges had been met and resolved to date. But the challenge of the Royal Gorge was far from met. First it had to be taken. And there were still the many miles to be covered, then the acute problem of raising an adequate crew. And trouble lurked just ahead, around a shoulder of mountain.

As Morley came around it, he saw first a roaring campfire, then a couple of men wrestling with a big wagon wheel, the wagon itself tilted crazily, and two droop-headed, hipshot work horses waiting patiently; and then a fat old man seated comfortably near the blaze shouting profane orders. It was he who yelled at Morley: "We need another hand here, neighbor," and caused Morley to rein the black down involuntarily.

Overhead a blanket of wet clouds began to drop a small drizzle. It also pinned down noises and did not let them escape into this night's darkness. Thus Morley was able to hear, faintly, the unmistakable wheezing of a steam locomotive. The sound was to him what a spur is to a horse, and he started on around the wagon, but one of the men let go the wheel, drew his gun, and grabbed King William's bridle, saying: "Whoa, now. I know this horse but I don't know the rider." The other man dropped the wheel and reached for his gun. The fat man grunted, rolled over, and pushed himself ponderously to his feet, bringing a rifle up with him.

Morley could arbitrate or he could fight his way out. It might be necessary to do both. And he might not succeed in either.

He said, "I needed a horse to carry me to Canon City. I bought this one from a young man in a poker game for three hundred dollars."

The fat man scratched his head. "Sounds a little like Joe Bentz, all right. Question: does he love gambling so much he would part with his King William? And what's your hurry, anyway?"

Morley took a moment to consider his reply. He knew that the eighteen hundred people of Canon City were sympathetic to the Santa Fe, and with reason: when D&RG ran its original track west of Pueblo, it had stopped at Labran, a coal-mining district eight miles east of Canon City. So the disappointed citizens of Canon City had raised $50,000 and asked the Denver and Rio Grande to build on. Their money ran out three fourths of a mile short of the edge of Canon City, and the track stopped. Canon City folk felt that the least the railroad could have done would be to run that short distance on their own, inasmuch as they would profit by it, too.

Morley tightened his legs around the big barrel of the black, imperceptibly lifting the lines, and felt the quick response—the readiness—under him. Then he gambled that this group was composed of Canon City people, and he said: "I'm from the Santa Fe. I want to get to the Royal Gorge before the D&RG does, but their work train is already so close you can hear it!"

The three tilted heads to listen. Plainly then, through the damp night, came the sound of the puffing engine. And the fat man yelled suddenly: "Let 'im go!"

Morley had to hold King William in after his lunging start. The moon, as though to help them along the way, suddenly appeared between a rift in the clouds. Somewhere a wolf howled in hungry loneliness, infinitely savage. The silver trunks of aspens stood out strongly against the black mass of spruce. An owl hooted, and then there was nothing but the thud of the horse's hoofs pounding the dampening earth of the road. In a little while of steady riding, Morley began to feel the accumulating weariness of the miles behind. Saddle muscles long unused began to complain. There was a growing pain up between his shoulder blades and a red-hot knife twisting in his side. In determined resolution he put his mind on the job ahead and crowded awareness of throbbing soreness out.

The Denver and Rio Grande was coming up behind him with a hundred men. Atmospheric conditions made it impossible to judge by sound how far behind him the train was. In his favor were the upward grade from Pueblo and the fact that McMurtrie and his men would still have to walk from the railroad into Canon City, and then a mile beyond. If King William held out, Morley should have time—barely enough—to raise a crew and get into the Gorge first.

But from where would he get the men? He recalled that Canon City had once had a choice of either the state prison or the state university, and they had chosen the penitentiary because it was an established institution and likely to be better attended. Would it be possible to borrow convicts temporarily? he wondered. Then a particularly hard nudge of pain under the rib cage stabbed him practical, and he said aloud: "You idiot! No warden would release his prisoners upon a peaceful countryside for the benefit of private industry."

The steady rain beat into his face and soaked through his

clothing, adding cold to his misery. King William stumbled. "Steady now," Morley said, and lifted the reins. The horse's head came up and he surged ahead, but Morley felt the raggedness now in the valiant animal's stride. His immediate problem became one of keeping King William on his feet. It was still far too distant to Canon City even to dream of reaching it on foot ahead of the D&RG. He forced himself to draw the black down to a walk, and was immediately glad he had done so, for the gnawing hurt between his shoulder blades and the twisting sword in his side both eased.

Such luxurious freedom from pain could not last. An errant current of air, flowing upward along the canyon of the Arkansas, brought him again the sound of a laboring locomotive, a steady, invincible, pulsing noise of exhaust and squeaking wheels. He lifted King William into a lope again—tired flesh and blood against hot iron and cold steel. To ride was torture, every faltering step of the horse beneath him put his body on a rack of pain. Exhaustion began to fog his vision and numbed his mind. The effort he was making became dreamlike. Time lapsed and then it dragged, but he kept moving forward in something near stupor.

Then King William fell. He went first to his knees, throwing Morley far out. He lit on his feet, but his knees were stiff and his hip joints locked, so he fell. The fall jarred him fully awake. He walked back to King William and tried to rouse him with gentle words and by lifting his head. The horse tried to get up, sighed, and fell back. He was dead. Morley turned at once and began to run.

Now he could be grateful for the unrelenting drizzle, for this cool and moisture-laden air. He sucked it deep into lungs that soon seemed to be filled with sharp bits of shattered glass. The silence of these foothills was broken by the thud of his boots against the damp earth and the bellows wheezing of his laboring lungs.

The thudding boots were handmade and had served him well and long. They were comfortable boots that had stood up to the rough work he had given them. But they certainly hadn't been designed for cross-country racing, especially not when the opponent was a clanking, belching, heartless assembly of nuts, bolts, rivets, boiler plate, and wheels.

The dim road he followed dropped sometimes to water's edge, at others climbed the river's banks. Each downward pitch was a gift to be blessed, while each upward slope was a diabolical drawback to be cursed, but even curses had to be said inside, for he hadn't breath enough available to mouth them. The knife that had been in his side gradually moved around to his chest to twist and stab with every step. He stumbled once where there was nothing in the road to stumble over. There was a pounding in his ears, but above it he thought he heard the senseless puffing of the steam locomotive, the insistent shriek of its whistle.

A darkened building loomed up on his right so abruptly that he shied away from it and almost fell. A stray moonbeam shone upon twin ribbons of cold steel—he had arrived at rail's end. That left him three fourths of a mile to go. Three thousand nine hundred and sixty feet. One exhausted man racing against a hundred who would be fresh and eager for action after the cramped quarters of the train. He would not let himself think about the ridiculous odds.

He remembered something that General Strong had once said about gambling: "I never bet on anything but cinches, but I bet all those freely." How was Strong betting tonight?

There were lights in the darkness now where there should have been no lights—bright pinpoints that came and went before his eyes. Then and there, Morley gave up smoking—every inhalation of tobacco smoke that he had ever taken was now exacting toll.

He had forgotten what he was doing and why. He would have run right through night-darkened, sleeping Canon City without seeing it except for the dogs. They came yammering at him from under houses to nip at his heels as his feet slapped the soft moist earth of the street. The canine chorus caused awakened citizens to come to their windows. One, closest to Morley, roared into the night: "What's going on down there?" and Morley stopped against a storefront.

He gathered all the strength that seemed left to him and put it into a vibrant shout that rang over the waiting housetops: "The Santa Fe is here!"

Like an echo, the announcement passed from mouth to mouth, house to house. Men, partly dressed, ran into the street with lanterns and surrounded Morley where he stood on trembling legs. A voice said, "Man, you look like you could use a drink," and a bottle appeared, but he brushed it aside. In the lanterns' yellow glow he showed white-faced and exhausted, but still very much the leader of men. The determination blazing from his steady eyes and set jaw passed on to the men around him as he spoke. Told them what he wanted of them—nay, *expected* of them!

One gray-bearded man answered for all: "We got a rumor of what was about to happen. We *want* to help. We have formed the Canon City and San Juan Railway, made a survey of the Gorge, and we have filed a plat. We're ready to turn the canyon over to you."

"How many men can you gather to help hold it?" Morley croaked.

"Fifty. They will gather in the Gorge with tools and guns. No one here is going to surrender tamely to the Denver and Rio Grande. You can bet your bottom dollar on that."

On this quiet night, sound crept into the silence that followed his words, and the men distinctly heard the train squeaking and jolting to a stop, three quarters of a mile away.

Morley said, "They'll be taking their time. Open the saloon, delay them longer. Each man bring along a short length of black pipe." Then he asked for a horse and wagon, and although the gray-bearded man argued that they could handle it from here, Morley knew he could not sleep until he had established Santa Fe's claim to the Royal Gorge. He went on alone.

Back at the D&RG terminal, the hundred enemy milled around, joking, having a big time, out on a lark. They picked out their gear from the boxcar it had ridden in and struck out after McMurtrie for the walk up to the Gorge. McMurtrie, confident that he had beaten the Santa Fe, feeling that their long ride entitled his men to a drink, set them up in the Canon City saloon. He had slept all the way up from Pueblo, but had he been thinking clearly he might have asked himself why a saloon in a quiet small town like Canon City would be open at two o'clock in the morning. But he had been lulled by the division superintendent's report of turning down Morley's request for transportation, and how else could men be brought timely to the Gorge?

So when the sun was well up and they finally rounded a bend in the approach to the Royal Gorge and were able to see Morley and about forty men digging busily in the rocky bottom of the canyon, they were taken completely by surprise. They assembled around McMurtrie, who urged them to attack. "Fight!" he shouted. "That's what you are here for!"

But they had seen men with rifles on the near walls of the canyon, seen other invisible riflemen behind black barrels poked out of underbrush and around rocks. Each man in McMurtrie's party felt that each weapon was sighted in on him, personally. They knew a capable ambush when they saw one, and wanted no part of this one. Their feeling went from amazement at finding Morley here to uneasiness and apprehension and suddenly, like frightened ducks leaving a pond, they turned as one and began the walk back to Canon City, ignoring McMurtrie's pleas and cajoling.

He advanced alone. Morley met him and said, "This Gorge is occupied by the Canon City and San Juan Railway, Mac."

McMurtrie said, "Rayme, you and I know there is no such company. You have fooled my men with those pieces of black pipe stuck in the brush, but not me. I think every man you have is in sight, and we outnumber you two to one!"

Morley's tired lips cracked into a smile. "Then don't let your belief make cowards of you. We're ready!"

So, much more quietly than they had arrived, the Denver and Rio Grande's men withdrew. When the last of the contingent had vanished down the road, Morley found a convenient thick bush to keep the rain off of him, lay down on his side, and immediately slept.

The battle for the Royal Gorge is amply reported in the pages of railroad history. Bat Masterson, among others, came down from Dodge City with a group of gunslingers to draw fighting men's wages and never do a lick of physical labor. Other men were hired out of the rough towns of the mining and cattle frontier. Blood was shed, and the war went into the courts. In a way, Santa Fe lost—but in another, the company won. The Denver and Rio Grande got the Gorge, but only after an out-of-court settlement; they bought out Santa Fe's claim for nearly two million dollars. And, as wily General Strong pointed out at a banquet honoring Morley for his part in securing the Gorge for Santa Fe: "Gentlemen, where else could we have gotten a better return on our initial investment—which was a two-hundred-dollar horse!" Strong then presented Morley with a gold-mounted Winchester Repeating Rifle. Morley worked the lever with characteristic caution to clear the chamber of this presumably "unloaded" gun before he took the General's handclasp.

There were still "railroads to be built" and Morley went on to build them. Three years later he finished the railroad from the International Line at Nogales to the port of Guaymas on the west coast of Mexico. Ada, still the lovely long-legged blonde girl, had the honor of tapping the little golden spike into place at the joining-up ceremony. And as grateful Nogalians named the main street of their town Morley Avenue at another banquet in his honor, Ada smiled at him with pride. At his ease in top hat and tails, he had come a long way from the boy she had first known, who had milked the president of Iowa State's cow. It was one more triumph for the engineering genius who had just turned thirty-eight.

A little later, in another wild and rugged place, he entered a two-seated hack and found himself staring right down the barrel of a .30-30 carbine. It was propped against the back of the driver's seat, and Morley requested that it be moved. The driver said, "It's not loaded," but Morley insisted. The lines had become tangled around the stock, so the driver jerked them to free them.

William Raymond Morley, who had not been afraid to face a hundred men with loaded guns, died under the hammer of the only thing in the world that he *did* fear—an "unloaded" one.

The Business
of Making Money

BY AGNES WRIGHT SPRING

*Even in the most turbulent territorial days, businessmen—especially
bankers—were a practical lot, viewing their fellow frontiersmen with
a realistic and wary eye. Probably for this reason, their uncolored and
meticulously kept records, where they have survived, present the most
accurate portrayal of their time and place available to the modern
reader. Nor is it to be supposed that these records are as dry as the
dust from which they have emerged. This was a time of high risk and
unavoidable adventure for all men, and survival for an enterprise was
as lusty an effort as it was for the most flamboyant individual. And
fatalities were apparently frequent. Western businessmen became of
necessity, therefore, men of considerable daring, great ingenuity, and—
when fortunate—prophetic vision.* —T.W.B.

WOULD it be possible for Clark, Gruber & Company, a
private banking house, to convert gold dust into coins?
This was the question E. H. Gruber asked his banking partner,
Milton E. Clark, in Leavenworth, Kansas, in the autumn of 1859.

Clark, a lawyer, looked up various authorities and gave as his
opinion that there was no law in the United States which could
be construed against the coining of money by individuals, provided the coin was made full weight. Mr. Gruber also consulted
two of the most prominent attorneys in Kansas Territory about
the matter. Both agreed with Mr. Clark.

The previous spring E. H. Gruber, a native of Hagerstown,
Maryland, employed in the bank of Isett, Kerr & Co., of Leaven-

Compiled from *The First National Bank of Denver. The Formative Years 1860–1865*
by Agnes Wright Spring, 1960.

worth, Kansas, had entered into a banking partnership with
Milton E. and Austin M. Clark.

On March 8, 1859, the Leavenworth *Daily Times* announced:

River News.
New Banking House.
Clark, Gruber and Company make their bow to the public this morning in
their splendid rooms at the corner of Delaware and Third streets. This new
banking house is established on a solid basis, and the enterprising gentlemen
having it in charge enjoy our best wishes for success as they launch their
gallant craft upon the public tide. We call attention to their card which ap-
pears in another column.

The "card" read as follows:

Banking Houses
Clark, Gruber & Co.
Bankers
and
Dealers in Exchange and Gold Dust,
Leavenworth, Kansas
Land Warrants, Foreign Coin, Uncurrent Money,
Bills of Exchange, Checks, Certificates of Deposit
and
Foreign Exchange
In sums to suit, on all parts of Europe.
We also issue Certificates of Deposit, which answer
as Exchange Throughout the Gold Mines
Clark, Gruber & Co.
Mar 8 dtf   Brick Building, cor. Delaware and Third
1859

Coincident with the organization of the new banking firm,
William H. Russell, of Russell, Majors and Waddell and John S.
Jones completed plans for launching a transportation company
known as the Leavenworth and Pike's Peak Express. This was
to be the first substantial, scheduled transportation facility into
embryonic Denver City. The initial outlay was $300,000.

Although rumors of gold having been found in the Pike's
Peak country had been current for a year or more, the real rush
to the Rockies did not begin until the spring of 1859. By early
April some ten or twelve hundred persons were encamped along
the banks of Cherry Creek and the South Platte River at Auraria
and Denver City, where they impatiently waited for the snow to
go out of the mountain gulches. They were restless and eager

to be off on the search for "colors." They were the advance of an army stretching across the plains from the Missouri River to the foothills of the Rocky Mountains.

But while immigration poured into the mining country, it also poured out with almost equal rapidity. Hundreds of half-starved and sadly disillusioned "go-backers" struggled to make their way eastward to their homes. They believed the gold rush to be a "humbug."

Spirits were lifted, however, when on May 7 two coaches of the Leavenworth and Pike's Peak Express, which had covered some 687 miles from Leavenworth in nineteen days, reached Denver. Next, spirits soared when word came that on May 6 John H. Gregory, a Georgia miner, accompanied by some "Hoosier" boys, had made a real discovery of gold in what is now the Central City area. This proved to be one of the richest lodes ever found in Colorado.

News of the so-called Gregory discovery and also of the discovery in January (made known at this time) by George A. Jackson on Chicago Creek, at the present site of Idaho Springs, spread rapidly. Despite frequent falls of rain and snow in May and up into early June, men pushed frantically toward the gulches.

When Horace Greeley, editor of the New York *Tribune,* reached the South Platte settlements in early June, he declared: "As to gold, Denver is crazy. She has been low in the valley of humiliation, and is suddenly exalted to the summit of glory. The stories of a day's works and rich leads that have been told me today by grave, intelligent men are absolutely bewildering."

With thousands of prospectors combing the hills and gulches and many of them extracting their only means of livelihood from the sands of the streams or from the quartz lodes, gold dust soon became the chief medium of exchange. Clark, Gruber & Company in Leavenworth increased their buying of the raw gold, as well as taking a considerable amount of it in payment for commodities at M. E. Clark & Company's wholesaling house on Cherokee Street. The company sold everything from sugar, teas, and fish to corn, oats, nails, and crockery for use on the Western frontier.

But this raw gold had to be shipped to the United States Branch Mint in Philadelphia to be coined into money. It was an expensive proceeding, as the only means of transportation from the gold fields to Leavenworth was by stagecoach. Clark, Gruber & Company had to pay 5 per cent of the value of the dust as an insurance against loss in transit, and another 5 per cent expressage. The dust was out of the company's hands anywhere from three weeks to three months. Often the cash that the company would have in transit would total nearly $300,000.

Other businessmen were experiencing the same inconvenience as Clark, Gruber & Company in handling gold dust. For instance, a report from the Philadelphia mint to J. B. Doyle & Company of Denver in October 1859 showed a loss of more than $100 on a shipment of gulch gold, valued as it was taken at Doyle's Denver store at $1009.

At this time, too, the miners were greatly disturbed over the fact that the merchants of Denver and Auraria had set a lower value on gulch gold than they had been paying. Mass meetings of protest were held in Russell's Gulch, and by the miners on Mountain City and the Gregory Diggings. At the last-named meeting on October 29 a resolution was passed which said in part: "We believe, and are well assured in our belief, that certain speculators in Denver and Auraria have sent some of the poorest specimens of retorted gold mixed with quartz to the mint to be coined, which they could by any possibility obtain for the purpose of swindling mountain men and miners. . . ."

Unquestionably the time was ripe for setting up a sound banking business in the new mining country that was seven hundred miles from its seat of government in eastern Kansas. Quietly having looked into the matter of minting, Clark, Gruber & Company felt that there was real need for coins to be minted in Denver in order to eliminate waste in the transportation of the gold dust.

A few bank advertisements had appeared in the *Rocky*

Mountain News of Denver thus far in 1859, but they were for firms in Chicago, Omaha, Nebraska City, and Council Bluffs.

General William Larimer, who had organized the Denver Town Company and had been instrumental in laying out and naming the new townsite, returned home to Leavenworth in October 1859 after a year's absence. He was well informed about the work that was going ahead in the various mining areas such as Russell and Gregory Gulches, South Park, the upper Arkansas Valley, over on the Blue, and on upper Clear Creek. He knew that the citizens of the Denver area were discussing the building of good wagon roads, that companies were planning extensive developments with heavy machinery, and that great freight trains were arriving almost daily and were discharging loads of supplies and mining machinery.

The Clark Brothers and E. H. Gruber knew Larimer and unquestionably discussed the Pike's Peak possibilities with him. In December 1859 Milton E. Clark went to Philadelphia to procure the necessary machinery and apparatus for converting raw gold into coins.

On January 18, 1860, Marshall M. Jewitt, a member of the original Denver Town Company, who had accompanied General Larimer to the Pike's Peak country in 1858, deeded for $600 three lots in Denver City to Clark, Gruber & Company. These lots were "known on the platt of said Denver City K. T. as lots Thirty-one and Thirty-two (31 & 32) in Block Forty-two 42 Lot Twenty 20 in Block Twenty (20)."

Early in January 1860 the Kansas Territorial Legislative Assembly met at Lecompton. In his message to the Assembly, Governor Medary dwelt at length on the matter of banking. The Governor stressed the importance of absolute integrity in banking relations.

This Assembly passed a private act which was approved by the Governor on February 27, 1860, which declared Austin M. Clark, E. H. Gruber, and their associates "a body politic and corporate . . . to be entitled . . . the Leavenworth and Pike's Peak Exchange Company." The act provided "That said company shall have authority to buy and sell exchange on Denver City, San Francisco, and other points westward of Leavenworth City, and on the towns and cities in the states east of the territory; *to buy and sell gold dust, and smelt and convert the same into ingots,* either at Leavenworth City, in Leavenworth County, or in Denver City, in Arapahoe County, or at any other point west of the twenty-five degree of west longitude that may, in the judgment of the said company, seem proper."

Section 10 provided that "Within Arapahoe County this company may collect whatever interest on money loaned the parties may contract for in writing."

No evidence has been found to show that the Leavenworth and Pike's Peak Exchange Company functioned under that name. Its officers, however, functioned as Clark, Gruber & Company, a copartnership in the banking business.

In February 1860 the Kansas Assembly also granted a charter to the Central Overland California and Pike's Peak Express. This new company, backed by Russell, Majors and Waddell, took over the Leavenworth and Pike's Peak Express and provided Denver with triweekly stagecoach service.

M. E. Clark & Company's wholesaling house was near the principal headquarters of the mammoth company of Russell, Majors and Waddell, whose government contracts and freighting operations throughout the Western country reached annually into the millions of dollars. With freighting trains constantly coming and going from the Rocky Mountains much firsthand information relative to the Western gold fields was accessible to the Clark Brothers and E. H. Gruber.

With direct river connection with St. Joseph, Missouri, Leavenworth was a natural gateway to the Great West. Having grown from one shack in 1854, its population now reached ten thousand. The town was just three miles down the "Big Muddy" from Fort Leavenworth, the principal supply depot for military stations as far west as Utah and New Mexico. At that time the crest of the Rocky Mountains was the western boundary of Kansas Territory.

Clark, Gruber & Company carefully guarded its plans for the establishment of its new branch bank and coinage department in Denver until the time arrived for actually going into action. Nothing in the local press forecast such a business until the arrival of L. L. Todd in Denver on March 30. On April 4 the *Rocky Mountain News* announced that Mr. Todd had come to Denver to make preparations for the establishment of an Assay and Coinage Office. It said: "He informs us that their machinery is all in readiness to ship from Leavenworth, about the 10th inst."

Heavy rains and high water delayed the proposed shipment somewhat. On April 20, the Leavenworth *Daily Times* printed the following:

Important Enterprise

Messrs. Clark, Gruber & Co., bankers of this city, last evening sent out to the mining region the entire machinery requisite for an assay office and mint for the coinage of eagles, double, half and quarter eagles. The apparatus is very complete and will be used in connection with the branch of their banking house, which these gentlemen are about establishing in Denver. A splendid safe and other appurtenances for the transaction of the latter department of the business was also forwarded at the same time. The whole goes out in charge of M. E. Clark, Esq., the senior member of the firm.

This is a project of no little consequence to the inhabitants of the gold country and it is fortunate for them that it has been undertaken by a firm whose standing is as high as that of Clark, Gruber & Company. We trust the enterprise will be entirely successful.

In the meantime, L. L. Todd was busy supervising the erection of the new banking house, assay and coining establishment at McGaa Street and G. It was a large two-story brick building on a stone basement, erected at an expense of upwards of $5000. When completed early in July it was said to be the showplace of Denver. The building had a frontage of twenty-five feet and it was forty feet deep. The walls of the basement which opened out on level ground at the back end of the building were two feet thick. The upper story had four rooms, plastered, eleven feet high. The second story, level with the street in front, was thirteen feet high. There were four double doors in front. Side doors and a stairway back led up to the third floor. A well-finished circular oaked counter and four desks were on the ground floor used as the banking office. Only the basement floor was used for coining. The third floor was a private apartment. The lot on which the building stood was fifty by 125 feet, inclosed by an eight-foot-high board fence. There was a good well supplying ample water for all purposes.

The largest machine was the coining press, which applied the dies to the milled planchet and thus stamped both sides of the coin. An intermediate machine cut or punched the planchets or disks of metal from a strip of gold rolled to width and thickness suited to the intended coin. The smallest machine was the milling machine which corrugated the rim of the coin and raised its edges.*

During the spring immigrants poured into Denver at the rate of two hundred a day. Covered wagons and tents filled up all available places. They clustered around buildings, sprawled in outlots and huddled along the banks of Cherry Creek. At night a thousand campfires flickered in the dusk for several miles.

Too, a great number of Indians were in and around Denver at this time. They were for the most part Arapahoe and Cheyenne disposing of buffalo robes and peltries. They were reported to be "peaceably disposed," though it was admitted that they did have access to whisky now and then.

By mid-June immigration began to change in character. Nearly all of the arrivals now were families with their household goods and gods, prepared to make permanent homes. Most of them brought ox teams, cows, and other stock. According to Editor William N. Byers of the *News,* on June 6: "Our city . . . has in a few months increased to a city of 6000 people; with comforts, and even luxuries of civilization. Ladies promenade the streets, arrayed in the newest, costliest silks from Stewarts'. . . . Lofty buildings are rising on the business streets; solid and substantial brick edifices of which old cities might well be proud. . . . Great trains of huge prairie freighters arrive and depart almost daily and more than a thousand emigrant wagons arrive each week. . . ."

For some time Clark, Gruber & Company had been issuing

---

* The original machinery now is on exhibit at the Colorado State Museum of the State Historical Society of Colorado, Denver, Colorado.

bills of exchange on the East for the gold dust they were buying. So large were their operations that a writer for the St. Louis *Democrat* called attention to the fact that because of the company's heavy buying only a limited amount of dust was then reaching St. Louis. "They will," the writer said, "refine all obtainable gold and run it into slugs and bars of convenient size, with their relative values stamped on them. They will thereby create a system of exchange somewhat similar to that used in the earlier days in California."

During July, Clark, Gruber & Company was constantly in the limelight, as the insides of the banking house and assay office were finished, the engine set up, and the coinage machinery installed for operation. On July 4 the *News* reported: "In a few days they will begin the manufacture of the much prized 'American Eagles.'" A week later, Editor Byers announced that he had seen specimens of "their coin in copper," and knew that they had begun coining gold.

Although Denver welcomed all of its pioneer bankers, an especial flurry of excitement was created when Clark, Gruber & Company invited editors and others to visit their minting room to witness the process of stamping the first coin from Pike's Peak gold.

Editor Byers' report of the visit appeared in the *Rocky Mountain News* on July 25, 1860:

In compliance with which invitation we forthwith repaired to the elegant banking house of the above firm, on the corner of McGaa and F [G] streets, and were admitted to their coining room in the basement, where we found preparations almost complete for the issue of Pike's Peak coin. A hundred "blank" had been prepared, weight and fineness tested and last manipulation gone through with, prior to their passing through the stamping press. The little engine that drives the machinery was fired up, belts adjusted, and between three and four o'clock the machinery was put in motion, and "mint drops," of the value of $10 each, began dropping into a tin pail with a most musical "chink." About a thousand dollars were turned out, at the rate of fifteen or twenty coins a minute, which was deemed satisfactory for the first experiment.

The coins—of which none but ten-dollar pieces are yet coined—are seventeen grains heavier than the U.S. coin of the same denomination. . . . The coin has a little of the roughness peculiar to newness but it is upon the whole, very creditable in appearance, and a vast improvement over "dust" as a circulating medium. . . . Any amount of the "wheels" can now be had at C. G. & Co.'s counter.

Editor George West of the *Western Mountaineer* was equally enthusiastic. On July 25 he wrote:

Coining of Pike's Peak Gold. On Friday afternoon, in company with several other spectators, we had the pleasure of witnessing the coining of $1000 in Pike's Peak gold into ten-dollar pieces, at the banking house and assay office of Messrs. Clark, Gruber & Co. The coin, which we have already described in the *Mountaineer,* is nearly identical in size with the United States coin of the same denomination. It contains the same amount in gold as the government coin, and about 1 per cent of silver in addition. Its average value at the mint, therefore, will be ten dollars and ten cents. All who have seen it seem highly pleased with it, and general satisfaction is expressed that we are now to have a circulating medium more convenient than dust, and in regard to which there can be no dispute. The coin thus far has been eagerly sought for by persons desirous of sending it to their eastern friends, and it is perhaps the best demonstration that can be sent abroad, of the richness of the Pike's Peak country. It is the distinctive product of this region; and in the minds of reasonable men, the fact that a reliable and substantial firm has transported the extensive and costly machinery requisite for this undertaking, and useless for all other purposes, from the sea coast to the base of the Rocky Mountains, and put it in operation here, will be a sufficient guaranty for the extent and permanency of our mineral resources.

George W. McClure, an expert assayer and mechanic from Iowa, was in charge of the minting department.

In Clark, Gruber & Company's first advertisement, which appeared in the *Rocky Mountain News* on August 8, 1860, and in the *Western Mountaineer* on August 9, the company called attention to the fact that "We have in connection with our Banking House a Mint, and are prepared to exchange our coin for Gold Dust. The native gold is coined as it is found alloyed with silver. The weight will be greater, but the value the same as the United States coin of like denomination."

Within a month the company's banking house and assay office were going full blast. Said the *Rocky Mountain Herald,* August 11: "It is quite a sight to behold the bars of gold piled upon their table, worth about $1000 each."

By August 25, Clark, Gruber & Company was said to be receiving about $2000 in dust daily. Its advertisement in Sutherland's *Leavenworth City Directory* showed them operating as bankers in Leavenworth, Kansas, and Denver City, and dealers in exchange, bullion, gold dust, uncurrent money, land warrants, and foreign exchange on all parts of Europe. Their references included ten banks scattered from St. Louis to New York City.

During the week ending August 28, the company melted and coined about $18,000 in ten-, five-, and two-and-a-half-dollar pieces. As specimens of coinage these pieces were said to have been far superior to any of the private mint drops issued in San Francisco, and nearly as perfect as the regular U. S. Mint issues. According to the *News* the faces of the first five- and two-and-a-half-dollar pieces were a good imitation of the government coinage—the head of the Goddess of Liberty, surrounded by thirteen stars, with the firm name of "Clark & Co." on the tiara. The reverse of the coin was "occupied" by "our noble bird," encircled by the words "Pike's Peak Gold, Denver, 2½D." The fineness of the coin was 828½, and the excess of weight over U.S. coin was twenty-three grains in a ten-dollar piece. The value in gold was the same as government coin of like denomination, with an additional value in silver alloy equal to nearly 1 per cent. By deducting the cost of coining at the United States Mint, about one half of 1 per cent, the actual worth of the Clark & Co.'s coin was one half of 1 per cent more than any other coinage. Clark, Gruber & Company's "mint drops" soon became the principal currency of the entire Pike's Peak country. During the first three months of the company's coinage operations the minting machinery, driven by steam, ran day and night. Currency amounting to $120,000 was produced.*

That Clark, Gruber & Company had shown excellent judgment in establishing a branch of its banking business in Denver was proven by the unprecedented development of the little prairie settlement. Buildings went up in all directions with a rapidity that astonished even the oldest pioneers. In July 1860, within two weeks more than a hundred stores and dwellings were started and in less than a month many of them were either finished and occupied or nearly so.

At this time the paying mines were extensive enough to assure permanency to the settlement on Cherry Creek. Transportation

* The extremely rare sets of Clark, Gruber & Company's coins are highly treasured by collectors. A set presented to the State Historical Society of Colorado years ago was valued at $10,000. The First National Bank of Denver has a set on display.

facilities had improved to such an extent that the C. O. C. & P. P. Stage and Express advertised "through to Missouri River in six days." A messenger now accompanied each coach to protect the large shipments of treasure. Although it was not unusual for the coaches to carry $10,000 in the regular express box, aside from the dust carried by individual passengers, no record has been found of the robbery of any of these early treasure coaches by road agents.

During the autumn various banking companies' advertisements in the local Denver newspapers gave way to those of commission and storage houses. Many wagon trains, referred to as "serpents of the plains," arrived in Denver freighted with flour, sugar, bacon, coffee, and other staples. These trains usually averaged around twenty-six wagons. Among the largest trains to come in were those of Jones & Cartwright with forty-four wagons, and J. B. Doyle, with thirty-five wagons. Both trains had more than three hundred head of cattle.

With travel increasing there was much discussion of roads between Denver and "the River." One of the proposed routes was on the north side of the Platte from Julesburg to Cherokee City, a place just laid out in "Big Bend," fifty miles below Denver. The Smoky Hill Route already had been laid out.

As winter crept over the high plains many businessmen went eastward from the mining districts to visit their former homes, or to attend to some business. A passenger on one of the stagecoaches on November 1 was A. M. Clark, bound for Leavenworth, Kansas. Editor Byers of the *News* said: "A. M. Clark, the well-known banker, leaves for Leavenworth by this morning's Express designing to spend several weeks in the East. He has done much toward the development of this region and will carry with him the good wishes of a host of friends."

Beginning in November, 1860, Clark, Gruber & Company, Bankers, supplied a monetary report for the newspapers as a regular feature. This report gave changing prices for gold at the different mining districts, in addition to other pertinent financial data.

According to the report for November 16:

The average fineness of the gold now sold is when retorted, about 820, or $17 per ounce in the bar. The average loss in melting is about 8 per cent. The retorted gold loses, in melting, from 7 to 20 per cent, accordingly as it is well or poorly retorted. The fineness of the gold from the different mills ranges from 750 to 825, as the gold from different leads is more or less alloyed with silver.

Denver was now growing up in many ways. The Denver Chamber of Commerce was organized. Elder John M. Chivington was canvassing the city for subscriptions to build a Methodist Episcopal church. The Langrishes were appearing regularly in theatrical productions. Local news columns discussed the propriety of "keeping open house" and "making and receiving calls on New Year's Day," and called attention to various religious services being scheduled by Methodists, Catholics, and Presbyterians. Woolworth and Moffat on Ferry Street announced that they had a fresh supply of interesting reading matter including *Harper's Weekly, Frank Leslie's Illustrated Newspaper, Vanity Fair,* the Boston *Pilot,* and others.

Clark, Gruber & Company's monetary report published on January 7, 1861, in the *News* gave the coinage in their Denver mint from July 15 through December as $131,240.50. According to the report the banking house of Clark, Gruber & Company, in Leavenworth, during the months of November and December purchased $60,000 in dust from persons returning to the states.

The Eastern money market was beginning to tighten because of warclouds, and Clark, Gruber & Company predicted that in the coming year more raw gold would be sold to the company in Denver for minting instead of being shipped east to the U. S. Mint in Philadelphia.

Severe weather isolated Denver for several periods during the winter, but there was an excessive supply of all kinds of provisions, so no suffering resulted from the isolation. On January 26 the long-overdue C. O. C. & P. P. Express coach, which had left St. Joseph on January 15, arrived in Denver. This coach brought the news that Kansas had been admitted as a state, and that the amendment to organize what is now Colorado into the Territory of Jefferson had been stricken off. This, of course, was a great disappointment to those who had hoped to have the un-official Territory of Jefferson—the Pike's Peak area—recognized officially. Said the *News* on February 16: "Our opinion is that the people of the region will pay very little respect or deference to any legislation or official acts from that direction (Kansas). We either want a territorial organization or the privilege of 'playing it alone' for a little longer."

They did not have to wait. Colorado became a territory through Congressional action, on February 28, 1861. News of the passage of the bill for the organization of a territory was an-nounced in Denver the day of Lincoln's inauguration as Presi-dent.

In this spring of 1861 the banking house of Clark, Gruber & Company bought great quantities of gold dust. New dies were used for coinage with all four denominations of coins for this year following closely the general pattern of those of the United States. The 1860 coins had been almost pure gold, containing very little alloy. These, however, had proved to be so soft that they abraded rather rapidly. It was therefore decided to use more alloy in the 1861 coinage.

A report of the Mint at Philadelphia in July 1861 showed the coins of Clark, Gruber & Company to be from 815 to 838 thousands, with a weight "greater in corresponding pieces of the national coinage in order to make up for the deficiency of fineness. On the average," reported the Mint, "the pieces are found to be of professed value, or slightly over."

Almost three months elapsed from the time Colorado was declared a territory until the arrival on May 27, in Denver, of Major William Gilpin, newly appointed Governor. In the mean-time, on April 14, Fort Sumter had been fired upon. The Civil War was a reality.

For a year or more before the secession of the Southern states began, John B. Floyd, Secretary of War in President Buchanan's cabinet, had at great labor and expense, been transferring from Northern arsenals to the various forts in the Southwest all of the military supplies they would hold. Floyd, known to be in sympathy with the South, also sent into New Mexico a large number of soldiers of the United States Army. He put them under the command of officers known to be favorable to the Southern cause.

Means of communication were slow and the fact that Fort Sumter had been shelled did not reach New Mexico until early in May. Immediately a number of the regular Army officers who were stationed there resigned their commissions and hastened to Texas, which had seceded in February. Enlisted men could not resign; to leave their posts would have been desertion, so most of the enlisted men remained.

Among the resignees was Major Henry H. Sibley, who had been in command of Fort Union in northern New Mexico, some 318 miles south of Denver. Sibley knew intimately the location and conditions at all of the forts located 350 miles southward along the Rio Grande River.

When he arrived among his Confederate friends, he was made a brigadier general by President Jefferson Davis. Sibley, it is said, at once began to lay plans to invade New Mexico, Colorado, and the Far West. With a brigade he planned to capture the forts up the Rio Grande; take Fort Union; then march north to Colorado's gold fields, where he expected to take over the Clark, Gruber Bank and Mint in Denver. He would then push on to the Oregon-California Trail, going to Fort Laramie in what is now Wyoming. Westward and southwestward from there he would go to Utah, where he was confident of cooperation from the Mormons, who had been in constant conflict with the Federal government.

Beyond Utah, which then included part of Nevada, lay the golden state of California with its great geographical extent, its mineral and agricultural wealth, and its coastline from which trade could be had with Asia. California's elective officers were known to be Secessionists or at least to be in favor of "benevolent neutrality."

Through this bold campaign, which Sibley and his fellow Confederates felt sure would be successful, control would be gained of three main transportation arteries into the West: the Santa Fe Trail, the Smoky Hill Trail, and the Oregon-California-

Mormon Trail. Sibley not only knew New Mexico, but he had been in charge of transportation of supplies across the Plains for Colonel Albert Sidney Johnston's Utah Expedition of 1857.

During the summer and autumn of 1861 Governor Gilpin, himself a military man, concentrated upon enlisting, drilling, and equipping the First Regiment of Colorado Volunteer Infantry. By early fall the regiment was completely raised. The men, some accompanied by their wives, moved into Camp Weld, a thirty-acre Army post, located two miles up the Platte River from the center of Denver. Colonel John P. Slough, a Denver lawyer, was made commander of the regiment, whose members dubbed themselves "Gilpin's Pet Lambs."

Two companies of volunteer infantry, sent by Governor Gilpin in December, in answer to an appeal from the Governor of New Mexico, arrived in time to participate in the Battle of Valverde, which was conceded a Confederate victory.

Early in January, having learned that Sibley's brigade of three thousand men was sweeping everything before it in New Mexico, Gilpin rushed the Colorado volunteers southward. The men, who were called "Pike's Peakers" by the Confederates, made a forced march in bitter weather. They were said to have stood the ordeal better than the horses. Many of the animals "dropped dead in the harness in the road."

On March 25 Commander Slough moved his force out to Bernal Springs on the Santa Fe Trail. Between Bernal Springs and Santa Fe was Glorieta Pass, a transverse opening at the southern end of the Sangre de Cristo range.

For about two days there was desperate fighting in the canyon below the pass, including an artillery duel and hand-to-hand encounters by the infantry and cavalry. There were many charges by both sides, and many casualties. After a battle of seven hours on March 27, Slough ordered his troops to return to Kozlowski's Ranch at the eastern end of the canyon where the water supply was adequate.

After he had ordered the retreat he was quite astonished when a messenger from the Confederates suddenly appeared with a truce flag stating that Colonel Scurry of the Texans asked for a suspension of hostilities till noon the next day for the purpose of burying the dead and caring for the wounded.

The truce was granted, but Colonel Slough did not know the real reason for the truce request until Major John M. Chivington and his weary men stumbled into camp about ten o'clock that night. Early that morning Chivington with 430 officers and picked men had been ordered to go around the Confederates in a flank movement toward the Galisteo Trail; to make their way along the sides of Apache Canyon; and to learn all they could about the enemy's camp.

As Chivington led his men over rugged and precipitous terrain they suddenly saw the enemy's supply camp directly below them at the foot of a cliff. There were a supply train of about eighty wagons, a fieldpiece, and horses and mules in a secluded corral.

The men wanted to attack at once, but Chivington held them back for an hour while he and Lieutenant Colonel Manuel Chavis got the lay of the land. Then he gave the command to charge. The soldiers let themselves down the mountainside by means of ropes, halters, swinging from tree to tree, or in any way they could get down. With yells and whoops they terrified the teamsters and infantrymen on guard in the camp, so that the latter seized the horses and mules at hand and fled.

The Coloradoans worked like demons. They upset the wagons, then blew them up or burned them with their cargoes of ammunition, food, medicine, surgical supplies, officers' clothing, saddles, and the like. They bayoneted some six hundred horses and mules in a corral. They dared leave nothing for the enemy. They knew they could take nothing up over the cliffs. *C'est la guerre.*

With their supplies destroyed the Confederates were forced to retreat to Texas as quickly as possible. Hence, the fight at La Gloriéta Pass is referred to as the "Gettysburg of the West." The Southwest and the West had for the time being been saved for the Union. The mint of Clark, Gruber & Company would continue to turn out golden eagles under the Stars and Stripes.

The honor and integrity of the firm of Clark, Gruber & Company was never questioned by the public, but after the territorial government of Colorado had been organized and was functioning, there was general public discussion as to the propriety, if not the legality, of this coinage within the shadow of the new government.

Clark, Gruber & Company was not the only firm issuing coins and currency at this time. On June 27, 1861, the *News* announced that Parsons & Company of Hamilton (South Park) was preparing to begin the coinage of gold at that place. They planned to issue quarter- and half-eagles. Soon afterward C. A. Cook & Company, auction and commission merchants, issued so-called "shin plasters" worth twenty cents and fifty cents in trade. In mid-August a new coin of the denomination of five dollars, issued by J. J. Conway & Company of Georgia Gulch, was attracting much attention.

In the meantime the first Territorial Convention of the Republican Party was held at Golden on July 2, and passed a resolution declaring the necessity for a public mint in Colorado, and pledging to help procure it. Clark, Gruber & Company heartily favored the proposition, and began to work toward that end.

On July 15, E. H. Gruber arrived in Denver by stagecoach and went into action. When he left for the States on August 31, he carried with him two letters of considerable importance. One was a letter of introduction from Territorial Secretary Lewis Ledyard Weld to the Honorable Salmon P. Chase, Secretary of the Treasury of the United States. The other letter was from Governor William Gilpin to Secretary Chase.

In his letter Secretary Weld explained that E. H. Gruber, Esq., of the Banking House of Clark, Gruber & Company, of Denver and Leavenworth, Kansas, "long and favorably known to the country," was in Washington on a mission of great importance. He urged Secretary Chase to give careful attention to the proposition.

The important business which Mr. Gruber pursued was that of endeavoring to interest the United States government in the importance of establishing a branch mint in Denver, and of purchasing the apparatus and machinery then owned by Clark, Gruber & Company.

Mr. Gruber already had aroused sentiment in Colorado and a Joint Memorial of the Legislative Assembly of the Territory of Colorado, approved by Governor Gilpin on November 4, 1861, stressed the necessity for a government mint in Colorado.

Considerable interest was aroused in the proposed mint. Editorial articles appeared in local newspapers emphasizing the necessity for such an institution. Congressman Hiram P. Bennett of Colorado prepared a bill providing for an assay office or branch mint in Denver, which was approved by the Secretary of the Treasury.

In a report made by Secretary Chase to the President, which was transmitted to Congress, he stated that he had been assured by the Attorney General that no law had been violated by Clark, Gruber & Company in producing coins, but recommended that the existing coinage laws be so amended as to prohibit private coinage in the United States. He also recommended that a branch mint be established at Denver, and that authority be given for the purchase of the property of Clark, Gruber & Company for conversion into a branch mint of the United States.

Passage of the act providing for a branch mint was not easily accomplished, as there were many opponents who felt that the government with its depleted treasury, due to war conditions, should not attempt such a new venture. Nevada was eager for a mint, and had many political friends. Introduced on December 19, 1861, the bill finally became effective on April 21, 1862, when signed by President Lincoln.

An appropriation of $75,000 was made by Congress for establishing the government mint. The price asked by Clark, Gruber & Company for its building and minting machinery was $25,000.

On June 14 Salmon P. Chase, Secretary of the Treasury, appointed a commission to estimate the value of the property involved.

Clark, Gruber & Company continued its business as usual during the government inspections. Some businessmen favored the buying of another building than the Clark, Gruber building and there were many arguments pro and con. At a meeting held in Denver on August 29, A. M. Clark announced that satisfactory arrangements had been made with the Mint Commissioners for the sale of the mint and the building to the United States. "The terms of the proposed sale," he said, "are of such a character as to be fair for all parties concerned." A deed of conveyance was signed on November 20.

In late October Dr. O. D. Munson was appointed U. S. Assayer for the Denver mint and took "charge of the assaying and melting departments of Clark, Gruber & Company, and was ready to melt, assay, and put into bars whatever gold should be offered until the U. S. Mint went into operation."

The end, however, was not yet in sight—nor the $25,000. Since there was no district land office in which Clark, Gruber & Company could perfect the title to its Denver property, it was necessary for Congress to clear the title before the government would accept it. On March 3, 1863, Congress passed a special joint resolution to enable the Secretary of the Treasury to obtain the title to certain property in the City of Denver, Colorado Territory, for the purposes of the branch mint.

In a full report Clark, Gruber & Company sketched the history of its Denver minting and coinage business, stating that the total coinage had been $594,305.00, and that from July 16, 1860, to January 1, 1863, it had purchased $1,462,647.75 in gold. The report concluded by saying that the company had on special deposit and had shipped for other parties to the mint in Philadelphia large amounts not included in the report.

It was soon rumored that Clark, Gruber & Company had purchased the brick building on F Street, next to Hussey's Bank, where the company intended to move its banking business, as soon as the United States Mint was started. On April 9, 1863, the Comptroller's Office in Washington approved for payment a voucher for $25,000 due Clark, Gruber & Company.

In writing of the final sale of the company's minting business, Jerome Smiley said in his *History of Denver*:

Thus ended one of the most interesting episodes in the history of any city in this country. To the isolated, hard-working people of the new country it was of tremendous advantage; it guaranteed them full value for the results of their laborious toil in the mines; it supplied them with a circulating medium of definite, unquestioned worth; it afforded them facilities for exchange with distant places at nominal expense; and through it all honesty and integrity ruled every transaction. No finer business record has been transmitted to us than that of the old time banking and minting firm of Clark, Gruber & Company.

On May 22, 1863, the *Rocky Mountain News* called attention to the fact that Clark, Gruber & Company, bankers, had moved from G Street and had "reopened in elegant business style on F Street. . . . They transact as usual a most extensive business in every department."

During the year local newspapers contained many reports of activities in the "mines of Montana" and among those who became interested in the "far horizon" was Emanuel H. Gruber. On March 16, 1864, he withdrew from the firm of Clark, Gruber & Company and established a bank in Virginia City, Montana.

The Clark Brothers continued in business under the name of Clark & Company. Their success as bankers was fully demonstrated when on May 10, 1865, they announced that on that day they had transferred and merged their Denver house "into a National Bank under the name and style of the FIRST NATIONAL BANK OF DENVER."

And thus the First National Bank of Denver which is magnificently housed in a modern, streamlined building in the heart of Denver's financial district can claim to be the oldest continuously operating bank in Colorado. Through the years it has spiraled upward from its pioneer beginning during the Gold Rush to the Rockies to its present stature.

The Homeseekers

BY FRED GROVE

The last geographic portion of the American West to be officially "opened" was a wedge of the old Indian Territory in what is now Oklahoma which was purchased from the Cherokee nation and returned to the Federal rolls as public land. The occasion was unique on several counts. Reacquisition of title from the Cherokees was the first large-scale land negotiation with Indian proprietors in which the principle of fair value was admitted and honestly practiced. In fact, the price paid was sufficiently generous to enable the Cherokees to suspend tribal ownership, distribute the proceeds by family and individual, and make the difficult economic transition from "wards of the government" to the responsibilities and privileges of full, non-discriminatory citizenship. But the most remarkable innovation was the manner in which the newly available lands were distributed to potential claimants—a widely advertised "race," with starting line, gun, and ground rules (first come, first served) which has become known as the Cherokee Strip Stampede. —T.W.B.

ASA Banner started across Summit Street, held up for a wagon, and as it passed he saw the catchwords rippling on the patched canvas cover: OKLAHOMA OR BUST. But it was the faces that left a wake in his mind. The faraway look of the settler, and his plain-cheeked wife, hoping, too, and the shy, excited children. Afterward he crossed through ankle-deep dust to stand on the boardwalk outside the government land office and resume his vigil.

Some minutes later he made a restless turn inside the crowded, noisy office. "Takes about three days to reach the line by wagon," a clerk was explaining. "After you file your claim, you got six months to settle your family on it. . . . First person on a homestead has first claim. . . . Look for stone markers. . . . Be land offices at Guthrie and Kingfisher. . . ."

One by one, Asa scanned the sunburned faces and went out.

He watched while the afternoon wore away, while the wagon and horseback traffic thickened and people streamed in and out of the high-fronted stores and milled like cattle on the walks and raised a pall of dust over the broad street. Hawkers peddled water at ten cents a dipper. Men swapped horses. In the plain multitude tenderfeet drew stares, awkward in buckskin jackets, wide hats, and self-consciously toting heavy revolvers in new leather holsters.

Two boys carried a stout box from the City Hotel. Trailing them came a man of lordly air, a derby hat high on his head. He mounted the box and peeled off a bright, impressive map from a large bundle.

"Folks," he announced, his voice like a bugle as he waved the map, "they call it the Beautiful Land down there—the Promised Land—and that's what it is." A pause, a deliberate pause. Hundreds of heads turned and the voice picked up, resonant, convincing. "Finest farm country you ever laid eyes on . . . Why, they say the climate's a good deal like California's—neither too hot nor too cold. You betcha . . . There's only one drawback— and that's water. It's a mite scarce at times. But these maps I have here—drawn accordin' to the dee-tailed in-structions of a trusted old Indian scout—will show you exactly where the creeks and the springs are. Where the best claims can be found . . . All yours for just one dollar."

There was an erupting surge toward the map peddler, a chorus of voices. Wood cracked and he floundered to the walk, swarmed under.

Asa Banner watched without moving, cold to the land hunger that he saw flushing the expectant faces like a high fever. About him he heard the hum and wrangle of voices from a dozen states. Thousands of homeseekers were camped around Arkansas City. Yesterday and today, riding in from Caldwell, he had seen them all along the rutted road. By the morning of April twenty-second thousands more, afoot, would swell this small Kansas border town in hopes of finding seats on the southbound trains.

Again, he began a round of the stores and livery stables and wagon yards. He moved deliberately, uncomfortable in the suit binding his shoulders, feeling the heavy six-shooter bumping his hip. The broad sturdiness of his body often forced him to walk sideways through the shifting mass overflowing the walks.

At the City Hotel a man wedged in ahead of him. Asa tapped him on the shoulder. When the man ignored him, Asa placed a solid hand on his shoulder, sent him spinning off the walk, and heard the crowd yell approval. Finally Asa worked inside to the clerk's desk. The register lay open. He read it line for line, turning the pages back for a week, and stepped away, thinking: *No, he wouldn't be foolish enough to sign his real name. Yet . . .*

A man with tired, sizing-up eyes nodded to him and murmured, "There's a little game in the back. Like to sit in?"

Asa took an onward step, then swung around. "I might."

"Follow me."

In a smoky room off the hallway Asa saw four card players, all strangers, around a table. One put down his hand and rose, invitation fawning across his pallid features.

"Never mind," Asa told him. "I'm not sitting in." These vultures were as those he had noticed on the streets, flocked in to fleece the homesteaders and tenderfeet. Asa turned toward the door. It was closed and in front of it stood the first man.

"You're all alike," he ridiculed. "Nobody will take a sportin' chance any more."

"Call this a chance?" Asa said. "Get away from the door."

Stiffening, the man slid his right hand inside his vest. Asa stepped forward; the hand fell away. Asa, in close, seized the man's shoulder and threw him sprawling over a chair, and jerked open the door and slammed it shut behind him. Through it he could hear an unbroken cursing, but no one opened the door.

Going down the hallway, he saw an ample-bosomed woman regarding him from her doorway. One languid white hand rested against the doorjamb, the other on her hip.

"What's all the racket?" she asked in an indifferent voice.

"Seems we didn't agree," he said and would have gone on had

she not put out her hand, a gesture that was more inquiring than restraining.

She gave him a half smile. The skin under her dark eyes was no longer young, but neither was she as old as she looked. Her red lips were heavy, though well formed, and her mass of lustrous black hair looked carefully combed. Once, he thought, she had been pretty.

"Sounded like a roughhouse," she said, arching her eyes.

"Not much," he said.

"Well, you'll get nothing for your money down there from that two-bit bunch." She darted her scorn in that direction and laid a discerning look upon him. "At first I didn't take you for a farmer, but your hands give you away."

"I *am* a farmer," he said. "A pretty good one, I think."

Something almost forgotten seemed to spring into her face. "I like a man who says what he is," she said, on impulse. "Look, I run this place, such as it is. I know people. I'm seldom wrong about men, good or bad. Do . . . you need a grubstake?"

He shook his head no.

"Would . . . you like to work for me, here? Help me run this?"

"I won't be here long."

"Just another homesteader," she sneered, and the liveliness left her face.

"You're wrong there," he said. A thought was enlarging, causing him to wonder why he hadn't asked before. "But maybe you can tell me something."

"Shoot."

"I'm looking for a quick horse trader, fourflusher, and jack-leg lawyer named Harley Cade. Least he calls himself a lawyer." Feeling was seeping into his voice.

Her eyes showed him absolutely nothing yet he thought her mouth seemed to tighten a trifle. "What do you want with him?"

"It's a private matter," Asa replied.

"Isn't it always?"

"You know him?"

Her enigmatic eyes changed suddenly. "Enough. He'll be in

the new town of Mulhall the day of the opening. He may go on
to Guthrie. That will be the real town in the Territory."

"Depends on the pickings, huh?"

"I didn't say."

"That all?"

"Isn't that enough?"

He spoke his thanks and stepped to the door that opened into
the lobby. There he hesitated, hearing the voices and the
shufflings and stirrings; together, he thought, they were like a
hammering pulse for the restless thousands.

"Maybe you'll come back," she said softly.

He turned and looked at her. It was a long look, and then he
went out.

On the morning of the twenty-first, Asa Banner was riding
south toward the starting line, into a greening, grass-rustling
world rolling gently away under a bright quilting of wild
flowers. Ahead and behind him he could see a snake line of
crawling wagons, their bowed hoods seeming to drift as ships on
the emerald prairie sea of the Cherokee Outlet.

A new feeling took hold of him. Everything lay so open and
unspoiled after the old Illinois country that he knew. The air had
a sweet scent. Now and then clouds of quail and prairie chickens
rose in sudden whirrings. A line of trees sketched a creek's
distant course, gave the eye a mark against the vast spaciousness.
At times his lulled mind wandered to waving wheat and graz-
ing cattle. It was as though he fought a bewitchment, while
knowing that none of this waiting land could be his.

At the high-banked Salt Fork of the Arkansas he crossed on
planks laid over the railroad bridge. His gelding's running walk
soon left the wagons behind. Some miles beyond he came upon
a lone covered wagon pulled off the broad trail.

A rawboned settler, his rapid hammer strokes awkward,
pounded the loose tire rim of the right rear wheel. A young
woman stood by watching and out on the prairie a small boy
picked flowers.

Asa was nearly past when the pounding ceased and he heard

a high curse of pain. He looked back to see the man gripping his left hand.

Without hesitating, Asa reined across. "Maybe you folks need some help?" he said.

The woman, embarrassed, said, "He can fix it. Thank you just the same."

Meanwhile the man continued to press his hand and pump it up and down. "I don't know," he said.

Asa dismounted to examine the wheel and rim. "Felly and spokes need soaking, is all," he said after a bit. "Wood's shrunk. Believe I can get the rim back on for you." With spaced strokes he drove the rim into place, and seeing a roll of barbed wire tied to the underside of the wagon, he bent and broke sections of it with which he wrapped the iron tire to the wheel. As he did these things so natural for him, he could not fail to note the team of poor bay horses, the patched harness, and the rickety condition of the wagon. It was a hard-used outfit, also worn by neglect.

"Cuss the luck, anyway," the homesteader said, surveying Asa's finished work. His lean jaws moved and his stooped shoulders slumped even more. When he spoke he had a way of pushing out his lower lip, giving it a pendulous suggestion of chronic defeat. A moodiness, a discontent, lay behind his dark eyes.

"You'll make it to the line before dark," Asa assured him.

"Just my luck to have another breakdown."

Asa had mounted when the young woman said, "Dell, I believe you forgot to thank him." And to Asa, in apology: "I'm Emily Marcum. This is my brother, Dell Sutton."

"Half brother, you mean," Sutton scowled.

She might not have heard him as she said cheerfully, "And that's Billy. We're all obliged to you."

"That's not necessary. I'm Asa Banner, folks. Good luck."

He held up still a moment longer, seeing her gray dress, pale from many washings, her heavy shoes, and the reddish color of her hands, and in her tanned face small wrinkles which should not have been there; for, he decided, she wasn't more than twenty-five. Her eyes were between blue and violet, and she wore her auburn hair pulled back and knotted on her neck. The prairie breeze shaped the long dress about her slim body.

But his strongest impression was of her calm and unwavering cheerfulness, which he kept remembering as he rode along.

Later he discovered black dots moving in the far green distance, some in bunches, like milling cattle spread over the prairie, and among them a range of low white hillocks, some swaying, some still. Riding nearer, he caught a remote drone, like that of bees swarming around a hollow tree. Nearer yet, he heard the drone turn into clatters and rumbles, into voices carrying across open country, and the hillocks became wagon tops.

East and west, as far as he could see, the prairie and wooded draws bloomed with snowy wagon tops and tents. Everyone seemed to observe an invisible line; gazing south, he understood why. Out there blue-clad cavalrymen rode back and forth or had posted themselves, guarding the free country until high noon tomorrow, when they would release the tide of homeseekers.

Leaving the main trail, Asa clattered across a rock branch and, searching once more, rode slowly west through an army of parked wagons, buggies, carts, and horsemen. Retracing his way, he scouted east past the branch for several miles, without luck again, and swung west, thinking to water his horse and make camp. By now the sun was low. Smoke from early supper fires trailed keen hungering smells across the cool spring air. He sighted low clouds banking in the west. Rain, maybe.

He had not reached the branch when his attention went to a solitary wagon halted on the main trail. The miserable, drooping team looked familiar, and on the wagon's right side three figures, one a child, stood around the rear wheel. Asa pulled up, recalling the man. What was his name? Sutton . . . Dell Sutton? It was much easier to remember the woman's name: Emily Marcum. Well, her brother was a grumbler and a leaner.

Reflecting on that thought, Asa passed west to the rocky branch and watered his horse.

He was eating his supper of hot coffee, bacon, and cold biscuits when Dell Sutton drove his limping wagon some rods down the wooded branch and unhitched. Minutes later Asa saw Sutton chopping on a large elm, using a hand ax. Soon Sutton's sister appeared. She shook her head at his clumsy efforts and pointed to a sapling. When Asa looked again, Sutton was struggling to lash the cut sapling under the right rear axle.

Asa experienced a vague hesitation. If you gave a leaner a hand, he just leaned that much harder on you. Now he saw Emily Marcum leave her cooking to help her brother. Soon after, Sutton stood back to watch her.

In disgust Asa set down his tin coffee cup and walked across.

It was almost as though Dell Sutton had expected him, for he said, "I remember you said soak the wheel. That's what I aim to do, if I ever get the blamed thing off."

"Let me see what I can find," Asa said and went back up the draw. He returned carrying flat rocks which he piled under the axle. Two more trips and the axle rested on a stout base. Asa removed the nut from the hub, pulled the wheel free, hammered the rim on, and rolled the wheel to the little stream for soaking.

Not until he was returning to the wagon did his sense of irritation catch up with him. While he had labored, Dell Sutton had observed and commented on the sorry state of his luck.

"We're obliged to you again, Mister Banner," Emily Marcum said. "Won't you stay for supper?"

"Thanks," Asa said. "I've had mine."

"Will you come for breakfast?"

There was, Asa thought, little or no resemblance between her and Sutton; somehow he was glad to discover that difference, and he wanted no more of Sutton's company. Other perceptions caused him to delay. These people were bone poor. Asa had felt it in the lightness of the wagon when removing the wheel, and he saw it in the meager supper being prepared; in the woman's drawn face, in the boy's, and he was angered because he could not change it.

And so he declined and turned on his heel before she could insist.

Asa Banner watched evening let down, spreading rich purple over the scented prairie, and he heard the voices of the camped multitude, clear and full of hope:

"We'll cross the mighty river
We'll cross the river Jordan"

It occurred to him that those were family groups singing; strangers only hours ago, now drawn together by the promise of new land and beginning life over again. For some there wouldn't be enough homesteads to go around. Yet tonight, he thought, everyone was rich, lifted up, and made young again by the seeking. Now and then, from another direction, he caught strains of banjo music and barroom verses about a girl waiting at the end of the Chisholm Trail. He smiled to himself. Cowboys. They rode fast horses, they knew where the best claims lay. He could feel the wish to be one of them.

Unable to resist the voices, he strolled over to a large fire which the singers ringed. Standing back in the shadows, he saw toil traced in the upturned faces: chinch bugs and drought, good times and lean times. Among the faces were those of Emily Marcum and Billy. Around Asa men smoked and talked of tomorrow. He heard a familiar, discouraging voice:

"Look at them clouds a-buildin' up. We're in for a bad storm, I tell you. Listen to that thunder." It was Dell Sutton.

At that moment the voices soared louder. Conversation trailed off. A light breeze sprang up, damp, rain laden, its touch uneasy on the face. A common feeling seemed to seize the singers. A strange excitement.

Asa Banner felt it likewise. He had the unreality of seeing actors on a stage, of being affected despite his detachment.

Movement rippled through the little crowd. A high-shouldered man making his way toward the fire. A rake-handle shape, he was, greasy black hair dangling to his shoulders, his eyes wild and darting in the uncertain light. He mouthed something and waved his long arms, prophetic, ominous.

Asa made out "Hellfire and doom!" That was all. Suddenly the stranger took long-striding steps back the way he had materialized. The crowd shrank away, opening a path. In moments he disappeared.

Just then the first spattering raindrops fell. A woman near Asa screamed and touched hands to her face. He saw her jerk her hands down and stare at them. He saw her swift fear, as of seeing blood, and her melting relief, as if a spell had passed.

Pealing thunder scattered these weather-wise people. Before they could reach their wagons and teams, gusts of wind lashed the camp. Whipping canvas tops slapped and ripped.

Asa started forward. A running man slammed into him, rushed on. Asa hurried across. When he found Emily Marcum she was standing still, shielding Billy's face with her hands. Wordlessly Asa took her arm. She turned at his touch, and in the light from the flashing sky he could tell that she expected Dell Sutton.

By the time they neared the wagon the wind was hurling rain shot against their wet faces. Out of the flickering darkness Dell Sutton staggered, hands protecting his face. Asa left them and bent on toward his picketed horse.

He had covered but few rods when a crash and cries shot up behind him. He stopped. Another cry, a woman's, wheeled him about. He ran back to find the wagon blown over and the woman and boy struggling to lift it off Sutton, who was shouting at them.

Asa knelt, worked his hands under the sideboard. Heaving and grunting, he strained upward and Sutton scrambled out and stood up gripping his right arm. Asa forgot him while he set about righting the light wagon.

And then, as suddenly as it had struck, the prairie storm rumbled off, gone. The moon slid out, big and clear.

Afterward, in the lantern light, it was Emily who pushed the flat rocks in place every time Asa lifted the axle up another notch.

"You did a right good job," Dell Sutton said, sounding contrite.

Asa, soaked through, walked past without speaking. Finding dry clothing in his bedroll, he spread out his poncho, rolled in his blanket, and slept.

A bright morning dawned. After last night's violence, Asa

reckoned superstitious settlers would see the wide blue sky and the sparkling prairie as good omens. Yet by noon the frontier would vanish, and a kind of regret had its way with him.

While he gathered firewood, figures moved into his vision from down the draw: Emily Marcum and young Billy. She lifted her long skirts above the wet grass. Pleasure smoothed her face as she looked off across the open country. Her heavy shoes bothered him. No woman, he thought, should have to wear such footgear.

"We want you to have breakfast with us," she greeted him. At his hesitation she said earnestly, "We've put you to a heap of trouble, Mister Banner."

"Not at all," he said and changed his mind then. "I'll be glad to come. Thank you. And the name is Asa."

At breakfast Dell Sutton, his arm in a sling, appeared to enjoy indisposition. He talked freely of the day's prospects. "Emily will have to handle the team," he said. "I can't do a thing. She's some woman, Mister Banner. First thing she did this mornin' was put that wheel on all by herself. . . . Reckon you've got a certain part of the country in mind for your claim?"

"I'm not here for land," Asa said.

"Well, I sure am. All I been thinkin' about for a year. A body gets tired of keepin' store. No future. Land's the thing."

"It can be a hard taskmaster, too," Asa said reminiscently. "Breaking this prairie sod won't be easy."

"Now Emily's man was a right good hand at that. She lost him last year—pneumonia. That's another reason why we're here. I want her and the boy to have something."

Breakfast over, Dell Sutton drifted off to visit his neighbors. Asa could hear his nasal voice lifted high, recounting the story of his storm-toppled wagon and his miraculous escape from serious injury. It was unlikely that Sutton had been an important man in the past or would be in the future. But today, sharing in the seeking and hoping, he was no less than the other far-eyed comers.

As he thanked Emily Marcum for the meal, Asa saw a question in her eyes.

"It's time to say good-by again," she said, smiling a little. "I hope we can homestead near a town, so there will be a school for Billy."

"Mulhall will be the nearest town from here," he told her. "That's southeast. The railroad goes through it. Take bottom land if you can, for wood, water, and pasture."

"Mulhall? So you're going there?"

"Yes."

"Then?"

"I'll go home."

Her thoughtful expression formed. But she said no more and he walked back to his camp, aware of a vague discontent.

While the morning advanced, Asa Banner could sense the jostling impatience of the homeseekers. He packed up and rode to the line. Every tent was down. Hitched teams stood waiting. Men huddled in little groups, gesturing, pointing south, southeast, southwest, scanning maps. When a stranger approached, the talk switched abruptly. Almost every man carried a weapon. From saddles hung sharpened stakes with flags; these would be driven into the ground as the first act toward claiming a tract.

As the sun rose toward high noon, Asa saw Emily Marcum drive the wagon in close to the line. Billy sat between her and Sutton, who was reared back, head high. Asa looked at his watch: eleven-twenty. Now the crowd flowed forward to pack the starting place. Men and women on horses, in wagons, fringed surreys, on foot, a few on high-wheeled bicycles; some pushed carts.

A flurry of action ruffled the open prairie. Two cavalrymen were escorting a protesting rider back to the line. He shook his fist at them as they rode away, and shouting settlers in turn cursed him. He displayed his disdain by halting rods in front of the others, whereupon determined homesteaders, all armed, marched out and forced him to ride behind the line.

Asa heard a man complain, "Another damned Sooner. They been sneakin' in for weeks. By God, it ain't fair. Us folks who made the government open up this country ought to get choice quarter sections without a run."

Just minutes now. A lull settled. Men on high-strung horses, lined up near the front, jockeyed for position. Asa heard a throat-torn shout, a warning shout. Immediately the troopers fired pistols and with a rising roar the tide of settlers spilled over the green prairie. All at once the voices dulled, muffled in the massive rumbling and bumping. A river of yellow fog enveloped swaying wagons and buggies, turned fleeing horsemen into quirting specters.

Asa lost sight of the Sutton wagon. His own horse was galloping, for he had let it go when the line surged. Already some homesteaders were jumping down to plant their fluttering flags. A train hooted cheerfully. Far away Asa saw its scribbling smoke. He pulled in his horse and angled that way.

About that time he picked up the Sutton wagon again, noticeable because it held a slanting course to his left while other homeseekers were hurrying south and southwest. Emily Marcum had the poor team trotting steadily. He was suddenly troubled. A pity if in taking his advice she found no free land.

He followed the wagon, though staying well back. He kept telling himself there was no hurry for him, that he was unmoved by what he saw. Still, when he turned his head and his eyes met the glittering face of the prairie beckoning in all directions, he understood precisely why the movers and campers and down-and-outers had come. A little later he stopped to take the six-shooter from his bedroll and belt it around him. It still felt unnatural and cumbersome, so strange to him and his way of living that he had not worn it since Arkansas City.

Now the sun was slipping into afternoon. Ahead the prairie, rising, dipping, swayed again to straggling creek timber, and there, like a tired white bird, rested one lone wagon, small against the sweeping green of the rich bottom land. The Sutton wagon. Beside it stood flag and stake.

A quick pleasure coursed through Asa Banner and he rode faster toward the wagon, the uncropped grass brushing his horse's belly. Dell Sutton waved in recognition and ran out to meet him.

"Mister Banner!" he shouted. "We've got us a claim!" Sutton's arm swung free of its sling. His voice had a new ring. He stood straighter. His black eyes flashed. Triumph flushed his lean face. He looked ten years younger.

"Fine," Asa said, sharing Sutton's elation. "Fine."

"We've checked the markers," Emily Marcum said. "It's ours." Her eyes were shining. Young Billy was jumping up and down and exclaiming.

"See that big burr oak down there?" Sutton asked, pointing to the creek. "I'll dig my dugout there. Gonna start right away."

As Asa turned to see, two men trailed out of the brush and timber masking the small creek. Both carried rifles. They tramped to the wagon.

"Looks like you folks are a little late," the lead man said. He shoved his head forward, his heavy jaw set. A biblike beard covered the upper buttons of his shirt. Not a cruel-faced individual, but his eyes were shrewd and he backed up his belligerent manner by planting his boots wide and showing off the menace of his thick, sloping shoulders.

Dell Sutton's face was ash white. "There's my stake," he pointed. "Where's yours?"

The bearded man inclined his head vaguely to the east.

"It wasn't there when I walked over the claim," Sutton said. "And I didn't see you."

"That's not my lookout. This man will vouch for me. Now get off."

Asa waited for Dell Sutton to back down, and he saw Sutton's head sag bit by bit and he saw him stare at the ground. Sutton's mouth was trembling. His sister watched with an expression akin to sorrow and resignation.

Inch by inch, Sutton brought his head up. His lips were still quivering when he spoke: "No—this land is mine. I won't get off." His hands clenched. Sweat beaded his ridged forehead. He stepped forward.

"By God—" the other man blurted, astonished. He made a sudden motion with the rifle. Emily screamed.

Asa jabbed heels to the gelding, at the same instant seeing the man's startled eyes above the mossy beard, just before he heard and felt the jar of his horse's forequarters knocking the man down and loose from his rifle.

The second man ran dodging. Asa buck-jumped the gelding alongside and leaned low, tore the rifle free, hurled it into the tall grass, and reined around. That was when, late, he remembered his pistol, still holstered, and he touched it. He looked up to find Emily Marcum's eyes on him.

Sutton had the first intruder's rifle and was guarding him. "I'll file a contest," the man swore.

"You'll play hell," Asa said. "You're Sooners—you sneaked in early and hid out. I'm a witness for these folks. Now hit the grit."

The two drifted away in the direction of Mulhall. Dell Sutton took his eyes off them and thoughtfully considered the rifle, as if surprised at himself, and leaned it against a wagon wheel.

"You didn't bluff," Asa said, "so they won't bother you again." He eyed the sun and headed his horse southeast.

"Do you have to go?" Emily Marcum asked.

"I've come a long way."

She came even with his stirrup, and he saw her open expression. "Why do you think you have to kill someone? You're no gunman."

He had an answer and yet somehow he did not, and so he made no reply.

. . . Mulhall was an anthill writhing under the hot springtime sun. Frantic hammerings rose above the din. Flimsy frame buildings stood finished, clean and yellow; others were skeletons, taking form even as he watched, and the smell of the newly cut lumber flavored the red dust. Tents fronted on the wide street and grew on it as well, seemingly planted without reason, and their white tops speckled the distance on all sides of the brash settlement.

Asa Banner passed through the restless throng to the end of the street and rode back. Next to the Boomer Saloon, on a vacant lot, two men in derby hats occupied chairs behind boxes on which hung lettered signs: LAW OFFICE.

Asa's lips flattened. He rode faster. One man he dismissed at once. It was the other one, back turned, talking, gesturing, who looked faintly familiar. The man turned around. He wore a full beard and he was heavy.

Asa reined up, his tension ebbing. How did you find one man among thousands?

Not long afterward he rode to the depot, tied up, and mounted the crowded platform. "When's the next train?" he asked.

"Ten minutes."

Inside the boxlike building disgruntled homeseekers pushed and shouted for tickets to Guthrie and Oklahoma City. Watching the jostling line, as he had the faces on the platform, he sensed the futility of his coming here.

A roly, bush-bearded man turned, head bent over money and ticket. He carried a carpetbag. The gray eyes under the derby hat found Asa briefly, flecked away, before the man stepped past.

Something tugged on Asa's mind, a troubling elusiveness. He jerked. That fellow! He was one of the lawyers set up in business only minutes ago by the saloon.

Asa was rushing out, drawn by a thing he couldn't connect. The packed crowd around the door blocked his way, hid his view. Boots rapped the platform on his right. Elbowing a path, Asa gained the end of the building, but the face wasn't there. He jumped to the ground and ran to the rear of the depot. Just beyond, a stout figure was lumbering across the open prairie.

In pounding strides Asa closed in. The man whirled and stopped, feigning surprise, a near-handsome man with a fleshy face. A knife sheath rode on his belt.

Asa still wasn't convinced. He flicked out his left hand, knocked the derby off, and then he knew and he saw that knowledge strike across Harley Cade's eyes.

Asa drew his pistol. "You almost fooled me," he hacked. "That beard—that hat—and fat as a hog." He eared back the hammer.

Cade's skin showed chalk above the thick brown beard. His voice sounded hollow: "Remember . . . your sister . . . she came with me."

"She did. But you left her to die in Caldwell. She wrote me.

She and the baby were both dying when I got there—right after you pulled out."

"I'm here to make a stake. I was goin' back."

"You're lying. You saw me on the street back there. You're running."

Cade's eyes bugged. "What you aim to do?"

"Make you pay up, now. Great big."

Asa Banner raised the pistol. His face knotted. For long moments he held the pistol on Harley Cade, not understanding why he couldn't kill a man who deserved killing. Of a sudden he holstered the handgun, confused by the struggle taking place inside himself, unable to figure himself.

Next he knew, Cade was digging inside his coat. Asa crashed into him and he heard Cade grunt and the thud of Cade's revolver on the grass. Asa smashed Cade's face, a savage blow that squirted blood. Cade, his face contorted, his eyes wild, lunged back with drawn knife, and Asa saw in him the wish to kill.

That was when Asa Banner drew his pistol, tortuously slow at best, and shot Harley Cade. The slug drove Cade backward one step; his mouth opened in total astonishment before he fell.

Around Asa, quickly, excited voices spoke and he was conscious of faces as in a blur, none distinct. A man said: "We saw him come at you with that knife. You had to do it. What was it over—a claim?"

Asa was too numb and sick to speak. Where was the righteous satisfaction he was supposed to feel? He had none whatever. Presently a train whistled and he stood alone by the depot platform. A consciousness grew. By nightfall the shooting would be all but forgotten, one of many violent episodes which the mighty stream of the day's events had swept under.

Another thought flared as light streaking across the darkness of his mind. It warmed him. He mounted and saddled northwest.

Emily Marcum looked up from her cooking when he was yet some distance from the wagon, an alertness that told him she had been watching. She came running through the tall virgin grass, pulling at her skirts, now pushing at a strand of hair falling across her forehead. She ran until he reined in before her. Her eyes, sweeping over him, held an enormous relief.

"You better know this," he said and hesitated. "I found out I didn't want to kill a man, after all. Then I had to."

She stood quite straight and still, the soft swell of her breasts rising and falling, a tall young woman whose sudden exertion had flushed hidden prettiness to her plain face, whose parted mouth framed a sweet-lipped gravity.

"I believe you," she said, and as he swung down from the saddle and he saw the giving and the pain for him, he felt a powerful shock and he knew there never would be an end for either of them.

The Windmill Man

BY ALLAN R. BOSWORTH

When the mountain men sought out the highroads into the West they were but commencing a process of settlement and the creation of a distinctive kind of American which still continues today. Perhaps it is no longer readily apparent in the cities of the West, for they are cosmopolitan in our time. But in the mountains, the valleys, the rangelands of the high desert—beyond the billboards and jet runways—the Western community still survives. Here the individual remains paramount, his stature measured by the life he leads and the length of his shadow in the eyes of his friends and neighbors. They are an humble people, but they are proud, for there are still tall men among them.
—T.W.B.

MR. Bob wasn't an eavesdropper, and what he overheard at Charlie's Service Station was purely accidental. His pickup was on the grease rack when he saw pretty Linda Bradshaw pull her car up on the other side and Mr. Bob's own nephew, Bud Wilson, hop out.

"Please listen to me, Bud," Linda was saying. Probably Bud was in a stew about her going to the dance a couple of weeks ago with Mead Polk.

Bud slammed the door. "Forget it!"

"I guess how *I* feel isn't important!" she snapped back, and the gears clashed. "Good-by!"

Mr. Bob had raised Bud through high school and had been teaching him windmilling since he came back from the Navy. But now he felt like giving the boy a kick.

Charlie came back then from filling a tourist's tank, and

THE WINDMILL MAN by Allan R. Bosworth originally appeared in *Farm Journal*. Copyright 1951 by Farm Journal, Inc.

picked up the grease gun. "Tol Henley find you, Mr. Bob?" he asked. "He's got two windmills on the fritz, and his water's runnin' out mighty fast."

Mr. Bob nodded. "Seems like all the mills break down at once."

Everybody called him that. Probably because he was getting along—sixty-seven, now—and had been around here fixing windmills since he was a young man. He was still tall and as brown as Manuel Gomez, who, with Bud, made up his crew.

As he got out he saw Joe Bradshaw, across the street. Joe was Linda's father, and cashier at the Stockman's Bank. "Been looking for you, Mr. Bob," he called.

"Mr. Bob, we're fixing up a little surprise for Doc Quigley. Doc's been around here forty-some odd years, same as you. We're giving Doc a watch Thursday night. Want you to make the presentation."

"Me! Shucks, Joe, I ain't a speechmaker!"

"Just tell Doc, plain and simple, how we appreciate some of the things he's done."

Mr. Bob squinted into the sunlight, remembering. Nineteen sixteen. That was when they had the smallpox scare, and Doc bought the vaccine himself, and never got paid for most of it. Lots of things like that, and all the time he could have moved on to bigger fields.

"Well, I'll try. I've done about everything else. You know windmillin' used to be a kind of an odd job. Like the braggin' feller I once heard say: 'I'm a drinker, a fighter, a wild-horse rider, and a pretty good windmill man!'"

"Yes, I know," said Joe with mock seriousness. "Now don't you fall off any windmills before Thursday night!"

Bud sat silently beside him all the way home. When the truck turned into the back yard Mr. Bob's wife, Eva, came down the porch steps. "Steve Mackey's north divide mill dropped a valve!" she called out. "And Sam Carlson's mighty near out of water. And you're needed at Kramer's."

Mr. Bob counted. Besides all these, Mr. Bob had promised to

stop and grease the mill at Bill Lauterbach's ranch, five miles
west of town.

"Golly, I've got to jump over half the county!" he said, and
then remembered. "But I promised to be back Thursday. Good-
by, honey."

"Now you be careful, hear?" Eva said, holding up her cheek
for her kiss.

They picked up Manuel and Mr. Bob drove west on the pavement that ran the long mesquite-green valley. Finally, just before
they reached Bill Lauterbach's house, he spoke to Bud. "I don't
aim to horn in, Bud, but if a girl like Linda wanted to tell me
somethin'—like, for instance, why she went to a dance with
another man—"

Bud broke in belligerently. "Mead Polk's got a good job with
the Bureau of Animal Industry. What have I got to offer?"

"Well," said Mr. Bob, glancing at him, "you got two hands
and a strong back." Then he shut off the engine and leaned his
head out of the cab to listen to the Lauterbach mill.

Getting out, he peered at a small dust-covered sedan standing
by the ranch yard. "Say, that's Doc Quigley's car. Wonder who's
sick?"

Nobody answered. Manuel got out with a gallon can of windmill oil, but Mr. Bob took it from him.

He climbed the ladder, feeling it tremble with the thrust of
the rods, until Manuel had looped the wire bail over the handle
of the shut-off lever.

She ought to marry Mead, eh? he thought, and grinned. Then
another thought struck him. Bud felt that there was a gulf between him and Linda, and if there was, the width and depth of
it was Mr. Bob's fault. He hadn't ever made enough money to
send Bud to college, and now he was sort of committing Bud to
the windmill trade. Maybe it was all wrong.

He ducked through the manhole and descended the tower.
Manuel threw the lever free, the tail fan swung into the wind,
and the wheel picked up its burden. Mr. Bob pricked up his
ears. There was a thin wailing sound above the rattle of the
rods.

Then he located the noise. It came from the ranch house, and he saw Doc Quigley's bouncing figure come out of the door.

"Boy," Doc wheezed, coming toward him. "Seven pounds!"

"Well, I'll be dad-blamed!" drawled Mr. Bob.

"One of these days," Doc Quigley said, "if I get time, I'm going to figure out how many babies I've delivered."

"Tell me somethin', Doc," Mr. Bob called after him. "How come you to stick around this county so long?"

Doc Quigley gestured toward the house. "You tell me how I could leave!"

Mr. Bob watched the dusty sedan turn down the road and said to Bud: "There goes a *big* little man!" Then he said, "You drive."

They went fifteen miles off the highway to Steve Mackey's ranch, and Mr. Bob wondered: *What makes the difference between success and failure?*

He lifted the tackle from the truck while Manuel climbed the tower to unshackle the rods, and Bud went up under the platform to rig a pulley block. When the boy was down again, Mr. Bob was tying the rope to the front bumper.

"Funny thing about Doc Quigley and me," he said. "We come here the same year, me drivin' a wagon and a span of mules, and Doc in a shiny buggy with red wheels. We're about the same age, too."

He slid behind the wheel to wait while Manuel clamped the grab on the nipple of the first rod. "Of course," he went on, "Doc had been to school. A man with education is fixed to make more money."

Manuel signaled then, and Mr. Bob backed the truck until the next nipple was above the casing mouth, and a heavy wrench had gripped it under the flange. Then he gave slack, and Bud was unscrewing the first rod and pulling it clear of the tower.

Mr. Bob waited and thought. He could pull windmill rods with his eyes shut: in the old days he had a horse that knew just how far to go, and never traveled a foot farther. Now he kept reversing and going forward, while the pile of rusty rod lengths grew until they came up wet, and the last emerged with the valve missing.

At noon they squatted in the small shade of the windmill platform and ate.

Mr. Bob spoke, "Doc could have taken that job with the big hospital in San Antone."

"One o'clock, Señor Bob," Manuel broke in.

The urgency came that afternoon as they fished for the elusive valve with a grappling tool. Kramer and Henley still to go, and then Sam Carlson's new mill—it took time to put up a new windmill, even when all the parts were on the ground.

Sam needed water badly, and Mr. Bob toyed with the idea of letting the other jobs wait. That way he'd be certain of getting back to town Thursday evening. But no, best to take them as they came.

It was noon the next day before Steve Mackey's mill was pumping again. Trouble with the country was that there was so much of it: fifty miles to Tol Henley's. Mr. Bob climbed one mill and replaced a broken part while Bud held an electric lantern. They had the other one working Wednesday morning, and were fixing to jump over to Kramer's when Mrs. Henley called Mr. Bob to the phone.

There was no mistaking the anxiety in Sam Carlson's voice. "Mr. Bob," he pleaded, "I've got to have that mill up tomorrow! Had one little water hole down in the draw—been pullin' pore cows out of the mud there. I need you bad, Mr. Bob!"

"Be there by noon," Mr. Bob promised. Ed Kramer's place was on the way, but Ed had several mills, and could move his stock if one tank went dry. Mr. Bob reckoned Doc Quigley sometimes had to pass up folks; he'd take care of a busted leg before doctoring a sprained one.

Bud only grunted when Mr. Bob told him what they were going to do. When they turned into a rough road that climbed the rimrocks toward the Rio Grande, Sam was out on horseback to open the gate.

They bounced over a mesquite flat, and over the white rocks of a draw bed rimmed with scrub walnuts. Here was the rank, froggy smell of water-hole mud, and on the bank, white-faced cattle stood in what pitiful shade they could find, switching the horn flies and bawling thirstily.

Mr. Bob knew that in about one more day Sam would have to truck his cattle to water, or haul water to them.

The truck groaned up through a cut that had been dynamited in the rimrock and halted with radiator boiling. Mr. Bob clambered out. Yonder were the well casing and the leg anchorages protruding from their concrete, and here a pile of steel windmill frame, hot to the touch with sun. Manuel and Bud began sorting the uprights. Sam asked: "How long, Mr. Bob? Can you have her pumpin' by tomorrow evenin'?"

"Been studyin' somethin' out," said Mr. Bob. He saw Bud straighten and look down the hill at the thirsty cattle, and he waited a minute and then called to him. He said: "I've seen 'em like that. They go blind for a spell, and their tongues swell up and turn black."

Bud looked up at him. "Well?" he asked quietly.

"It's kind of up to you," Mr. Bob said. "Remember you was wonderin' if we couldn't assemble a steel tower on the ground and then raise 'er?"

He had no time to think about his speech. Here was a thirty-foot tower, with horizontal and diagonal braces cut to fit, and holes already bored. Mr. Bob let Bud take charge, and when the uprights were raised to the perpendicular each leg would be within inches of its anchor post. That way, they could bring the rods plumb in the well casing. Mr. Bob was all over it, sweating and straining. Sam stood around and fretted. "Never seen a windmill lyin' on its side before," he observed.

The sun dropped. "You boys come to the house for supper," Sam Carlson said. "You're too tired to cook."

Mr. Bob was tired, indeed, and as he lay awake he got to worrying a little about raising the tower. It weighed a lot, and if it fell before they got it on its legs, there'd be busted and bent steel all over the place. Still, it was time somebody used new methods in windmilling, same as in everything else. Finally he fell asleep.

The next morning Bud shackled an eight-foot length of three-inch casing at right angles to the end of each of the tower's upper legs. He ran a yoke from the tops of these to a cable in a pulley block secured to the ground. When the truck backed slowly, the leverage gained by the pipes tilted the tower and brought it upright until it tethered and stood. It took but a few minutes to jockey it into exact position and bolt it there.

As Mr. Bob left the truck he saw that Bud was as modestly confident as ever, and a little feeling of pleasure went through him. Seemed like Bud was taking a real interest for the first time.

There remained the work of hoisting the heavy engine and wheel sections, but now they had the tower itself for a derrick. The engine was in place by noon. They ate hastily, and then Mr. Bob and Bud swarmed up the ladder again, while Manuel sent up the tail fan and wheel sections.

Mr. Bob wrestled and strained. He looked at his watch once, and shook his head. "Can't let Doc Quigley down," he said. "Still, I don't see how we can be through here till after dark, and then it's forty miles back to town."

He had a minute before the next wheel section came up, and he looked out over the next divide. The view suddenly surprised him: a man could stand on Sam's new windmill and see clear into tomorrow.

There were ten—twelve—fifteen windmills scattered around the horizon. That one way over yonder flashing in the sun like a bright spinning dime, was on the Patterson place. Yonder were two of Ed Kramer's—he had put both of them up. *Look all around the skyline and see windmills pumping water out of the earth for stock to drink. This country would be pretty near a desert without them. Look around and see a lot of old mills I had been doctoring when they were sick.*

He smiled to himself, wishing he could make Bud see it, too. The way it was, he and the windmills were a whole lot like Doc Quigley and the babies he had brought into the world. Doc had never gone to any bigger field, because he couldn't get clear of the need people had for him here at home. It was the same in the windmill business. *Mr. Bob, I need you mighty bad!*

And all at once he had the answer about success and failure. *It was how much a man was needed that counted.*

The last wheel section came up. When it was in place, he went down the ladder, spry for his age, to help get the rods in the well.

The sun went down. He stepped back and looked up at the mill; he said: "Okay, Manuel!" and the shut-off lever went free. The tail fan swung out, the wheel began turning.

Sam Carlson knelt, putting his ear to the casing. "Listen!" he shouted. "I can hear the water comin' up!"

Mr. Bob grinned, and mopped his bald head with a bandanna. Just then a dry bearing on the engine began squealing, and Bud seized a can of oil and started up the ladder.

"Wait a minute!" Mr. Bob called. "It's *my* baby. You run down to the house and phone Joe Bradshaw. Tell him I'm mighty sorry but I'm goin' to be too late."

Bud hesitated, and Mr. Bob grinned. "Maybe she'll answer the phone," he said. "And if I was you, I'd tell her I'd see her to-night."

Bud raised an eyebrow. "I'm beginning to think you know as much about hearts as Doc," he said. "As a matter of fact, she's answered already. I called her from Carlsons' after supper. It's something I was getting around to telling you, whenever I thought you could stand the shock."

It was after nine when Mr. Bob trudged heavily up the steps to the courthouse and sidled in the door. He was conscious of the four-day beard and his work clothes. A fine-looking character he was to make a speech, even if he'd been on time! He thought about the long ago days as he stood against the wall, trying to make himself small. Then he heard Doc Quigley talking.

"Well, it sure is a mighty fine gesture, and a mighty beautiful watch," Doc was saying. "And I see by it that it's time for me to run to Bill Metzger's and see if he needs some more blood."

People applauded, and looked after Doc as he came toward the door. Somebody yelled: "There's Mr. Bob, now!" and all at once Tol Henley and Bill Lauterbach grabbed him and dragged

him up the aisle. Everybody was standing, and he had a confused glimpse of Eva, her eyes shining, and then Bud and Linda
just to one side of her. And if he had thought Eva's eyes were
shining, why, they weren't anything compared to Linda's.

Then there was Joe Bradshaw. Mr. Bob stammered a kind of
an apology for being too late to make his talk, and Joe said never
mind, he'd made one himself.

Mr. Bob didn't hear half of what Joe said. It was something
about the good Lord knowing what He was doing when He
made Texas, putting the water so far underground and then
making the wind blow so hard, because He knew windmills
would be invented, and that Mr. Bob would come along to make
them run. It was something about everybody in the county wanting Mr. Bob to know how much he was appreciated.

Then he handed Mr. Bob a little box. Mr. Bob got it open
after a while, with his hands shaking, and it took a little longer
to wipe the mist out of his eyes so he could read the inscription
on the back of the gold watch.

It said: "For Mr. Bob, A Pretty Good Windmill Man—the
Best We Know."